Everyday
Mathematics®

Study Links

Everyday Mathematics

Study Links

The University of Chicago
School Mathematics Project

A Division of The McGraw·Hill Companies

Columbus, Ohio
Chicago, Illinois

UCSMP Elementary Materials Component
Max Bell, Director

Authors

Max Bell
John Bretzlauf
Amy Dillard
Robert Hartfield
Andy Isaacs

James McBride, Director
Kathleen Pitvorec
Peter Saecker
Robert Balfanz*
William Carroll*

Technical Art
Diana Barrie

First Edition only

Photo Credits

Phil Martin/Photography, Louis Renault/ Photo Researchers, Inc.
Cover: Bill Burlingham/Photography; Photo Collage: Herman Adler Design Group

Contributors

Tammy Belgrade, Diana Carry, Debra Dawson, Kevin Dorken, James Flanders, Laurel Hallman, Ann Hernwall, Elizabeth Homewood, Linda Klaric, Lee Kornhauser, Judy Korshak-Samuels, Deborah Arron Leslie, Joseph C. Liptak, Sharon McHugh, Janet M. Meyers, Susan Mieli, Donna Nowatzki, Mary O'Boyle, Julie Olson, William D. Pattison, Denise Porter, Loretta Rice, Diana Rivas, Michelle Schiminsky, Sheila Sconiers, Kevin J. Smith, Theresa Sparlin, Laura Sunseri, Kim Van Haitsma, John Wilson, Mary Wilson, Carl Zmcla, Theresa Zmcla

 This material is based upon work supported by the National Science Foundation under Grant No. ESI-9252984. Any opinions, findings, and conclusions or recommendations expressed in this material are those of the authors and do not necessarily reflect the views of the National Science Foundation.

www.sra4kids.com

SRA/McGraw-Hill

A Division of The McGraw-Hill Companies

Send all inquiries to:
SRA/McGraw-Hill
P.O. Box 812960
Chicago, IL 60681

Printed in the United States of America.

ISBN 1-57039-973-5

13 14 15 WAL 08 07 06

Contents

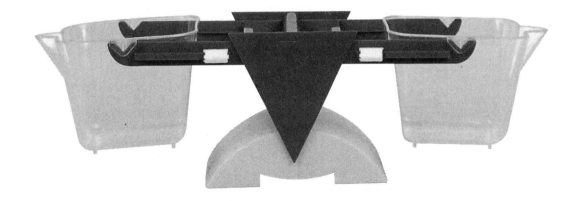

Introduction to Fifth Grade Everyday Mathematics

Welcome to *Fifth Grade Everyday Mathematics*. It is part of an elementary school mathematics curriculum developed by the University of Chicago School Mathematics Project. *Everyday Mathematics* offers students a broad background in mathematics.

Several features of the program are described below to help familiarize you with the structure and expectations of *Everyday Mathematics*.

A problem-solving approach based on everyday situations
By making connections between their own knowledge and their experiences, both in school and outside of school, students learn basic math skills in meaningful contexts so that the mathematics becomes "real."

Frequent practice of basic skills Instead of practice presented in a single, tedious drill format, students practice basic skills in a variety of more engaging ways. In addition to completing daily review exercises covering a variety of topics, patterning on the number grid, and working with multiplication and division fact families in different formats, students will play games that are specifically designed to develop basic skills.

An instructional approach that revisits concepts regularly
To enhance the development of basic skills and concepts, students regularly revisit previously learned concepts and repeatedly practice skills encountered earlier. The lessons are designed to take advantage of previously learned concepts and skills and to build on them throughout the year instead of treating them as isolated bits of knowledge.

A curriculum that explores mathematical content beyond basic arithmetic Mathematics standards around the world indicate that basic arithmetic skills are only the beginning of the mathematical knowledge students will need as they develop critical thinking skills. In addition to basic arithmetic, *Everyday Mathematics* develops concepts and skills in the following topics—numeration; operations and computation; data and chance; geometry; measurement and reference frames; and patterns, functions, and algebra.

Please keep this Family Letter for reference as your child works through Unit 1.

Fifth Grade Everyday Mathematics *emphasizes the following content:*

Numeration Recognizing place value in numerals for whole numbers and decimals, expressing numbers in scientific notation; finding factors of numbers; comparing properties of prime and composite numbers; representing rates and ratios with fraction notation

Operations and Computation Extending whole-number facts with addition, subtraction, multiplication, and division to fractions and decimals; evaluating symbolic expressions

Data and Chance Collecting, organizing, and analyzing data using bar graphs, line graphs, circle graphs, and stem-and-leaf plots

Geometry Investigating angles and rotations; calculating area and volume; drawing to scale; introducing relationships of 2- and 3-dimensional figures; exploring new transformations that affect attributes of geometric shapes

Measurement Using linear, area, capacity, and personal reference measures

Reference Frames Locating items with reference to an origin or zero point; for example, ordinal numbers, times of day, dates, and temperatures

Patterns, Functions, and Algebra Determining divisibility; exploring number patterns; applying formulas to geometric figures; creating number models; working with scientific calculators; squaring and unsquaring numbers; exploring variables in formulas

Everyday Mathematics will provide you with ample opportunities to monitor your child's progress and to participate in your child's mathematics experiences.

Throughout the year, you will receive Family Letters to keep you informed of the mathematical content your child will be studying in each unit. Each letter will include a vocabulary list, suggested Do-Anytime Activities for you and your child, and an answer guide to selected Study Link (homework) activities.

You will enjoy seeing your child's confidence and comprehension soar as he or she connects mathematics to everyday life. We look forward to an exciting year!

Unit 1: Number Theory

During the next 2 or 3 weeks, students will study properties of whole numbers. Unit 1 sets up procedures for review and practice of the multiplication facts. The new material in this unit builds on students' prior work with multiplication and division of whole numbers.

In Unit 1, students will be asked to collect pictures of arrays to form a class Arrays Museum. Pictures may include objects such as floor tiles, windows, and checkerboards. You may want to help your child find pictures to contribute. To practice using arrays with your child at home, use any small objects, such as beans, macaroni, or pennies.

Finally, you may want to help your child memorize the basic multiplication facts found in the multiplication table. You can work together using the Fact Triangles, or you may play *Beat the Calculator, Multiplication Top-It,* or *Baseball Multiplication.* These are games that were introduced in previous grades of *Everyday Mathematics.*

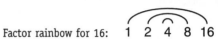

Vocabulary

Important terms in Unit 1:

composite number A whole number that has more than two factors. For example, 4 is a composite number because it has three factors: 1, 2, and 4.

divisible by One whole number is *divisible by* another whole number if there is no remainder when you divide.

exponent The small, raised number in *exponential notation* that tells how many times the base is to be multiplied by itself.

Examples

$5^2 \leftarrow$ exponent $\quad 5^2$ means $5 * 5$, which is 25.

$10^3 \leftarrow$ exponent $\quad 10^3$ means $10 * 10 * 10$, which is 1,000.

$2^4 \leftarrow$ exponent $\quad 2^4$ means $2 * 2 * 2 * 2$, which is 16.

factor One of two or more numbers that are multiplied to give a *product*. The numbers that are multiplied are called *factors*.

$$3 * 5 = 15 \qquad 15 * 1 = 15$$
Factors Product   Factors Product

factor rainbow A way to show factor pairs in a list of all the factors of a number. A factor rainbow can be used to check whether a list of factors is correct.

Factor rainbow for 16: 1 2 4 8 16

number model A number sentence that models or fits a number story or situation. For example, a number model for the array below would be $4 * 3 = 12$.

prime number A whole number that has exactly two factors: itself and 1. For example, 5 is a prime number because its only factors are 5 and 1.

product The result of mutiplying two numbers, called *factors*.

rectangular array A rectangular arrangement of objects in rows and columns such that each row has the same number of objects and each column has the same number of objects.

square number A number that is the product of a whole number multiplied by itself. For example, 25 is a square number, because $25 = 5 * 5$.

Building Skills through Games

In Unit 1, your child will practice operations and computation skills by playing the following games. Detailed instructions for each game are in the *Student Reference Book.*

Baseball Multiplication

See *Student Reference Book,* pages 259 and 260
Two players will need 4 regular dice, 4 pennies, and a calculator to play this game. Practicing the multiplication facts for 1–12 and strengthening mental arithmetic skills are the goals of *Baseball Multiplication.*

Multiplication Top-It

See *Student Reference Book,* page 295
Multiplication Top-It is another game used to practice the basic multiplication facts. This game requires a deck

of cards with 4 each of the numbers 1–10, and can be played by 2–4 players.

Beat the Calculator

See *Student Reference Book,* page 261
This game involves 3 players and requires a calculator and a deck of cards with 4 each of the numbers 1–10. Playing *Beat the Calculator* helps students review basic multiplication facts.

Factor Captor

See *Student Reference Book,* page 271
This is a game for 2 players. Materials needed include a *Factor Captor* Grid, 48 counters the size of a penny, scratch paper, and a calculator. The goal of the game is to strengthen the skill of finding the factors of a number.

As You Help Your Child with Homework

As your child brings assignments home, you may want to go over the instructions together, clarifying them as necessary. The answers listed below will guide you through this unit's Study Links.

Study Link 1.2

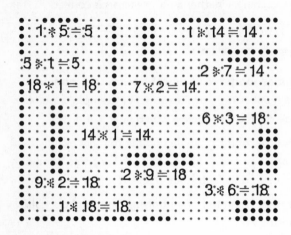

Study Link 1.3

6. 2, 4, 6, 8, 10, 12, 14, 16, 18, 20

7. Even numbers

8. Sample answers: 1, 3, 5, 7, 9, 11, 13, 15, 17, 19

9. Odd numbers

Study Link 1.4

1. 1, 5, 25

2. 1, 2, 4, 7, 14, 28

3. 1, 2, 4, 5, 8, 10, 20, 40

4. 1, 2, 3, 6, 7, 14, 21, 42

5. 1, 2, 3, 4, 6, 8, 12, 16, 24, 48

6. 1, 2, 4, 8, 16, 32, 64

7. 1, 2, 4, 5, 10, 20, 25, 50, 100

Study Link 1.5

1. numbers divisible by 2: 998,876; 5,890; 72,344; 36,540; 1,098

numbers divisible by 3: 36,540; 861; 33,015; 1,098; 45,369

numbers divisible by 6: 36,540; 1,098

numbers divisible by 9: 36,540; 1,098; 45,369

numbers divisible by 5: 5,890; 36,540; 33,015

numbers divisible by 10: 5,890; 36,540

2. numbers divisible by 4: 998,876; 72,344; 36,540

Study Link 1.6

2.

Number	Factors	Prime or Composite?
11	1, ⑪	P
18	1, ②③ 6, 9, 18	C
24	1, ②③ 4, 6, 8, 12, 24	C
28	1, ② 4, ⑦ 14, 28	C
36	1, ②③ 4, 6, 9, 12, 18, 36	C
49	1, ⑦ 49	C
50	1, ②⑤ 10, 25, 50	C
70	1, ②⑤⑦ 10, 14, 35, 70	C
100	1, ② 4, ⑤ 10, 20, 25, 50, 100	C

Study Link 1.7

1. 16   **2.** 49   **3.** 6   **4.** 64   **5.** 25

6. 81   **7.** $9 * 4 = 36$ **8.** $5 * 5 = 25$

9. a. $5 * 5 = 25$

   b. There are the same number of rows and columns.

     10. 13   **11.** 9   **12.** 113

Study Link 1.8

1. 64: 1, 2, 4, 8, 16, 32, 64   **2.** yes

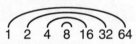

$8^2 = 64$ The square root of 64 is 8.

3. a. 4, 9, 25, 49

   b. They are the squares of prime numbers.

Study Link 1.9

1. a. $10^4 = 10 * 10 * 10 * 10 = 10,000$

   b. $7^2 = 7 * 7 = 49$

   c. $20^3 = 20 * 20 * 20 = 8,000$

2. a. 11^2 **b.** 9^3 **c.** 50^4

3. a. $2 * 3^3 * 5^2 = 2 * 3 * 3 * 3 * 5 * 5 = 1,350$

   b. $2^4 * 4^2 = 2 * 2 * 2 * 2 * 4 * 4 = 256$

4. a. $36 = 2 * 2 * 3 * 3 = 2^2 * 3^2$

   b. $40 = 2 * 2 * 2 * 5 = 2^3 * 5$

   c. $90 = 2 * 3 * 3 * 5 = 2 * 3^2 * 5$

5. 4^5

More Array Play

A **rectangular array** is an arrangement of objects into rows and columns. Each row has the same number of objects and each column has the same number of objects. We can write a multiplication number model to describe a rectangular array.

$4 * 3 = 12$

For each number below, use pennies or counters to make as many different arrays as possible. Draw each array on the grid with dots. Write the number model next to each array.

1. 5   **2.** 14

3. 18

Show each number model below as an array of dots.

4. $2 * 6 = 12$ **5.** $5 * 4 = 20$

> *Reminder:* Look for examples of arrays and bring them to school.

Factors

To find the factors of a number, ask yourself: Is 1 a factor of the number? Is 2 a factor? Is 3 a factor? Continue with larger numbers. To find all the factors of 15, for example, ask yourself:

	Yes/No	Number Sentence	Factor Pair
Is 1 a factor of 15?	Yes	$1 * 15 = 15$	1, 15
Is 2 a factor of 15?	No		
Is 3 a factor of 15?	Yes	$3 * 5 = 15$	3, 5
Is 4 a factor of 15?	No		

You don't need to go any further. Can you tell why?

_____

_____

_____

The factors of 15 are 1, 3, 5, and 15.

List as many factors as you can for each of the numbers below.

1. 25 _____

2. 28 _____

3. 40 _____

4. 42 _____

5. 48 _____

Challenge

6. 64 _____

7. 100 _____

Play *Factor Captor* with someone at home.

Divisibility Tests

- All even numbers are **divisible by 2.**
- A number is **divisible by 3** if the sum of its digits is divisible by 3.
- A number is **divisible by 6** if it is divisible by both 2 and 3.
- A number is **divisible by 9** if the sum of its digits is divisible by 9.
- A number is **divisible by 10** if it ends in 0.
- A number is **divisible by 5** if it ends in 0 or 5.

1. Use divisibility tests to check whether the following numbers are divisible by 2, 3, 5, 6, 9, or 10.

Number	Divisible ...					
	by 2?	by 3?	by 6?	by 9?	by 5?	by 10?
998,876						
5,890						
72,344						
36,540						
861						
33,015						
1,098						
45,369						
4,009,721						

A number is divisible by 4 if the tens and ones digits form a number that is divisible by 4.

Example 47,8**36** is divisible by 4, because 36 is divisible by 4.

It isn't always easy to tell whether the last two digits form a number that is divisible by 4. A quick way to check is to divide the number by 2, and then divide the result by 2. This is the same as dividing by 4, but it is often easier to do mentally.

Example 5,3**84** is divisible by 4, because 84 / 2 = 42 and 42 / 2 = 21.

Example 9**22** is not divisible by 4, because 22 / 2 = 11, but 11 / 2 = $5\frac{1}{2}$.

Challenge

2. Put a star next to any number in the table that is divisible by 4.

Factor Rainbows, Squares, and Square Roots

1. List all the factors of each of the square numbers. Make a factor rainbow to check your work. Then fill in the missing numbers. *Reminder:* In a factor rainbow for a number, the product of each connected factor pair should be equal to the number itself. For example, the factor rainbow for the number 16 looks like this:

1 2 4 8 16

$1 * 16 = 16$ $2 * 8 = 16$ $4 * 4 = 16$

Example 4: 1, 2, 4 1 2 4 $2^2 = 4$ The square root of 4 is 2.	**9:** $\_\_^2 = 9$ The square root of 9 is __.
25: $\_\_^2 = 25$ The square root of 25 is __.	**36:** $\_\_^2 = 36$ The square root of 36 is __.
49: $\_\_^2 = 49$ The square root of 49 is __.	**64:** $\_\_^2 = 64$ The square root of 64 is __.
81: $\_\_^2 = 81$ The square root of 81 is __.	**100:** $\_\_^2 = 100$ The square root of 100 is __.

2. Do all square numbers have an odd number of factors? _____

Challenge

3. a. Which square numbers in Problem 1 have exactly 3 factors? _____

   b. What do they have in common? _____

Exponents

An **exponent** is a raised number that shows how many times the number to its left is used as a factor.

Examples

5^2 ← exponent 5^2 means 5 * 5, which is 25.

10^3 ← exponent 10^3 means 10 * 10 * 10, which is 1,000.

2^4 ← exponent 2^4 means 2 * 2 * 2 * 2, which is 16.

1. Write each of the following as a factor string. Then find the product.

Example $2^3 = \underline{2*2*2} = \underline{8}$ **a.** $10^4 = $ _____ = _____

b. $7^2 = $ _____ = _____   **c.** $20^3 = $ _____ = _____

2. Write each factor string using an exponent.

Example $6 * 6 * 6 * 6 = \underline{6^4}$ **a.** $11 * 11 = $ _____

b. $9 * 9 * 9 = $ _____   **c.** $50 * 50 * 50 * 50 = $ _____

3. Write each of the following as a factor string that does not have any exponents. Then use your calculator to find the product.

Example $2^3 * 3 = \underline{2 * 2 * 2 * 3} = \underline{24}$

a. $2 * 3^3 * 5^2 = $ _____ = _____

b. $2^4 * 4^2 = $ _____ = _____

4. Write the prime factorization of each number. Then write it using exponents.

Example $18 = \underline{2 * 3 * 3} = \underline{2 * 3^2}$

a. $36 = $ _____ = _____

b. $40 = $ _____ = _____

c. $90 = $ _____ = _____

Challenge

5. Which is greater, 5^4 or 4^5? _____

Family Letter

Unit 2: Estimation and Calculation

Computation is an important part of problem solving. Fortunately, we are no longer restricted to paper-and-pencil methods of computation. We can use a calculator to solve lengthy problems, or even a computer program to solve very complex ones. Throughout the year, students will have many opportunities to practice estimation, mental, and paper-and-pencil methods of computation; to use a calculator; and to decide which method is most appropriate for solving a particular problem.

Many of us were taught that there is just one way to do each kind of computation. For example, we may have learned to subtract by "borrowing," without realizing that there are many other methods of subtracting numbers. In Unit 2, students will examine several methods for adding, subtracting, and multiplying whole numbers and decimals. From these exposures to a variety of methods, they will see that there are often several ways to accomplish the same task and achieve the same result. Students are encouraged to solve problems by whatever method they find most comfortable, even if it's one that they themselves may have invented. However, there is one method for each operation that all students will be expected to learn.

The class will also work on the first **Estimation Challenge** of the year. This is a problem for which it is very difficult, time consuming, and perhaps even impossible to find an exact answer. Students work with partners or in small groups to come up with and defend their best estimates. Estimation Challenges will be presented several times during the school year.

Your child will also learn a new game—*Multiplication Bull's-Eye*—which provides practice with estimation. You might want to play this game with your child at home. The rules of the game are found on page 284 in the *Student Reference Book*.

Computation is usually not the first step in the problem-solving process. One must first decide what numerical data is needed to solve the problem and which operations need to be performed. In this unit, your child will continue to develop his or her problem-solving skills with a special focus on writing and solving equations for problems.

Please keep this Family Letter for reference as your child works through Unit 2.

Vocabulary

Important terms in Unit 2:

Estimation Challenge Sometimes your child will be asked to solve a problem for which it is difficult, or even impossible, to find an *exact* answer. Your child will need to make his or her best estimate and then defend it. We call this kind of problem an *Estimation Challenge*.

magnitude estimate A very rough estimate. A magnitude estimate tells whether an answer should be in the tens, hundreds, thousands, and so on.

Example: 56 * 32

Step 1: Round 56 to 60.

Step 2: Round 32 to 30.

60 * 30 = 1,800, so the magnitude estimate for 56 * 32 is in the thousands.

10s	100s	(1,000s)	10,000s

maximum The largest amount; the greatest number in a set of data.

mean The sum of a set of numbers divided by the number of numbers in the set. The mean is often referred to simply as the *average*.

median The middle value in a set of data when the data are listed in order from smallest to largest. If there is an even number of data points, the median is the *mean* of the two middle values.

minimum The smallest amount; the smallest number in a set of data.

partial-sums method A way to add in which sums are computed for each place (ones, tens, hundreds, and so on) separately, and are then added to give the final answer.

```
        268
      + 483
1. Add 100s        600
2. Add 10s         140
3. Add 1s        +  11
4. Add partial sums. 751
```

Partial-sums algorithm

place value A system that values a digit according to its position in a number. In our system, each place has a value ten times that of the place to its right and one-tenth the value of the place to its left. For example, in the number 456, the 4 is in the hundreds place and has a value of 400.

range The difference between the *maximum* and *minimum* in a set of data.

reaction time The amount of time it takes a person to react to something, such as having a hand squeezed.

trade-first method A subtraction method in which all trades are done before any subtractions are carried out.

100s	10s	1s
	4	12
3	~~5~~	~~2~~
− 1	6	4

Trade 1 ten for 10 ones.

100s	10s	1s
	14	
2	~~4~~	12
~~3~~	~~5~~	~~2~~
− 1	6	4
1	8	8

Trade 1 hundred for 10 tens and subtract in each column.

Building Skills through Games

In Unit 2, your child will practice operations and computation skills by playing the following games. Detailed instructions for each game are in the *Student Reference Book*.

Baseball Multiplication

See *Student Reference Book*, pages 259 and 260

Two players need 4 regular dice, 4 pennies, and a calculator to play this game. Practicing the multiplication facts for 1–12 and strengthening mental arithmetic skills are the goals of *Baseball Multiplication*.

Beat the Calculator

See *Student Reference Book*, page 261

This game involves 3 players and requires a calculator and a deck of cards with 4 each of the numbers 1–10.

Playing *Beat the Calculator* helps students review basic multiplication facts.

Multiplication Bull's-Eye

See *Student Reference Book*, page 284

Two players need 4 each of the number cards 0–9, a six-sided die, and a calculator to play this game. *Multiplication Bull's Eye* provides practice in estimating products.

Multiplication Wrestling

See *Student Reference Book*, page 285

Two players need 4 of the number cards 0–9 to play this game. *Multiplication Wrestling* provides practice with multiplication of whole numbers.

Use with Lesson 1.10.

Do-Anytime Activities

To work with your child on the concepts taught in this unit and in previous units, try these interesting and rewarding activities:

1 Practice extending multiplication facts. Write each set of problems so that your child may recognize a pattern.

Set A	6 * 10	6 * 100	60 * 100
Set B	5 * 10	50 * 10	50 * 100
Set C	10 [7s]	100 [7s]	100 [70s]

2 When your child adds or subtracts multidigit numbers, talk about the strategy that works best. Try not to impose the strategy that works best for you! Here are some problems to try:

$467 + 343 =$ _____

$894 - 444 =$ _____

_____ $= 761 + 79$

$842 - 59 =$ _____

3 Write whole numbers and decimals for your child to read, such as 650 (*six hundred fifty*) and 42.5 (*forty-two and five tenths*). Ask your child to identify digits in various places—thousands place, hundreds place, tens place, ones place, tenths place, hundredths place, thousandths place.

4 You may want to discuss with your child how data are collected in real life. Discuss how the following probability statements might have been obtained.

- "About 2 out of 3 adults can swim." (*By asking a large number of people if they can swim.*)

- "There is a chance in 100 that a home will catch on fire during the next year." (*By using fire reports to estimate the number of house fires per year.*)

As You Help Your Child with Homework

As your child brings assignments home, you may want to go over the instructions together, clarifying them as necessary. The answers listed below will guide you through this unit's Study Links.

Study Link 2.1

1. L	**2.** L	**3.** OK
4. S	**5.** OK	**6.** S
7. L	**8.** S	**9.** OK	**10.** S

Study Link 2.2

Sample answers are given.

1. The numbers 571 and 261 should be circled.

2. The boxes with the numbers 30, 20, and 7 should have Xs in them.

3. The boxes with the numbers 19 and 23 should have check marks in them.

4. The boxes with the numbers 533 and 125 should have stars in them.

5. The boxes with the numbers 85.2, 20.5, 88.2, and 17.5 should have triangles in them. Since the sum has ".7" in the tenths place, look for numbers with tenths that add to 0.7. $85.2 + 20.5 = 105.7$; and $88.2 + 17.5 = 105.7$.

6. 4,572   **7.** 4.4   **8.** 246   **9.** 1.918

Study Link 2.3

1. The numbers 451 and 299 should be circled.

2. The boxes with the numbers 100.9 and 75.3 should have Xs in them.

3. Sample answers: The boxes with the numbers 803 and 5,000 should have check marks in them.

4. The boxes with the numbers 17 and 15 should have stars in them.

5. The boxes with the numbers 1,500 and 703 should have triangles in them.

6. The boxes with the numbers 9 and 25 should have smiley faces in them.

7. 61   **8.** 137   **9.** 5.8   **10.** 18.85

Study Link 2.4

2. **a.** 14.08 and 11.85
   b. How much more Julie paid for gas in Chicago than in Iowa
   c. 14.08 − 11.85 = g
   d. 2.23   **e.** $2.23

4. $27.23 + s = $34.98; $7.75

Study Link 2.5

Answers vary for Problems 1–5.

Study Link 2.6

Sample answers are given.

1. Unlikely: 30%   Very likely: 80%
   Very unlikely: 15%   Likely: 70%
   Extremely unlikely: 5%

2. 30%: Unlikely   5%: Extremely unlikely
   99%: Extremely likely   20%: Very unlikely
   80%: Very likely   35%: Unlikely
   65%: Likely   45%: 50–50 chance

Study Link 2.7

2. The 1,000s box should be circled.
   10 * 700 = 7,000

4. The 10,000s box should be circled.
   10 * 6,000 = 60,000

Study Link 2.8

2. 930; the 100s box should be circled.

4. 21; the 10s box should be circled.

6. 2.26; the 1s box should be circled.

Study Link 2.9

2. 3,100; the 1,000s box should be circled.

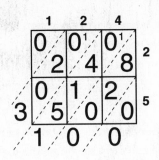

4. 33.372; the 10s box should be circled.

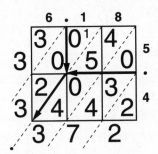

6. 341.61; the 100s box should be circled.

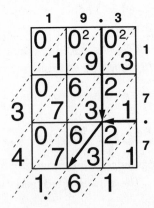

Study Link 2.10

1. **a.** yes   **b.** no   **c.** more

2. **a.** 350 cups   **b.** Sample answer: 18,000 cups

3. About 926,100 quotations

Use with Lesson 1.10.

Estimating Measurements

For each statement below, mark whether the measurement given is

S: too small   **OK: reasonable**   **L: too large**

_____ **1.** The width of the teacher's desk is 5 yards.

_____ **2.** A paper clip weighs about 3 kilograms.

_____ **3.** The length of an adult's step is about 2 feet.

_____ **4.** The distance between New York City and Los Angeles is about 670 miles.

_____ **5.** The length of a craft stick is about 10 centimeters.

_____ **6.** A full bathtub holds about 50 cups of water.

_____ **7.** The diameter of a penny is about 7 inches.

_____ **8.** It would take about 2.5 minutes to walk a mile.

_____ **9.** The temperature in Chicago during the summer is about 84°F.

_____ **10.** Most people like to drink soft drinks at a temperature of about 0°C.

Open Sentences and Number Stories

SRB
209 211
221–223

For each problem on this page, fill in the blanks and solve the problem.

1. Althea and her brother collect baseball cards. Althea has 148 cards. Her brother has 127 cards. How many cards do they have altogether?

   a. List the numbers needed to solve the problem. _____

   b. Describe what you want to find. _____

   _____

   c. Open sentence: _____

   d. Solution: _____   e. Answer: _____
   (unit)

2. Julie was driving from Chicago, Illinois, to Topeka, Kansas. Before she started, she ___ed her tank with 10 gallons of gas. She paid $14.08. After driving about 305 miles, she stopped for gas in Iowa. Again, she got 10 gallons of gas and paid $11.85. How much more did she pay for gas in Chicago than in Iowa?

   a. List the numbers needed to solve the problem. _____

   b. Describe what you want to find. _____

   _____

   c. Open sentence: _____

   d. Solution: _____   e. Answer: _____

3. Mark paid for his burger and fries with a $20 bill. His burger cost $3.89; his fries cost $1.49. How much change did he receive?

   a. List the numbers needed to solve the problem. _____

   b. Describe what you want to find. _____

   _____

   c. Open sentence: _____

   d. Solution: _____   e. Answer: _____

Circle the open sentence that best matches the story. Then solve the problem.

4. Ralph and Adeline saved their money for 6 weeks. Ralph saved $27.23. Adeline saved $34.98. How much more did Adeline save than Ralph?

   $27.23 + \$34.98 = s$ $6 * s = \$34.98$

   $27.23 + s = \$34.98$ $6 + s = \$34.98 - \$27.23$ Answer: _____

Comparing Reaction Times

Use your Grab-It Gauge. Collect reaction-time data from two people at home. One person should be at least 25 years old.

1.

Person 1	
Left	**Right**

2.

Person 2	
Left	**Right**

3. Median times:

Left hand _____

Right hand _____

4. Median times:

Left hand _____

Right hand _____

5. How do the results for the two people compare to your class data?

_____

_____

_____

_____

How Likely Is Rain?

Many years ago, weather reports described the chances of rain with such phrases as "very likely," "unlikely," and "extremely unlikely." Today, the chances of rain are almost always reported as percents. For example, "There is a 50% chance of rain tonight."

1. Use the Probability Meter Poster to translate phrases into percents.

Phrase	Percent
Unlikely	*30%*
Very likely	
Very unlikely	
Likely	
Extremely unlikely	

2. Use the Probability Meter Poster to translate percents into phrases.

Percent	Phrase
30%	*Unlikely*
5%	
99%	
20%	
80%	
35%	
65%	
45%	

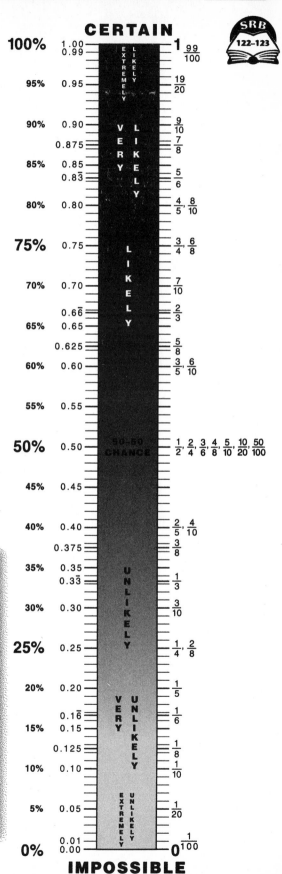

CERTAIN

100%	1.00 / 0.99	EXTREMELY LIKELY 1 99/100
95%	0.95	19/20
90%	0.90	9/10
	0.875	7/8
85%	0.85 / 0.83̄	5/6
80%	0.80	4/5, 8/10
75%	0.75	3/4, 6/8
70%	0.70	7/10
	0.66̄	2/3
65%	0.65	
	0.625	5/8
60%	0.60	3/5, 6/10
55%	0.55	
50%	0.50	50-50 CHANCE 1/2, 2/4, 3/6, 4/8, 5/10, 10/20, 50/100
45%	0.45	
40%	0.40	2/5, 4/10
	0.375	3/8
35%	0.35 / 0.33̄	1/3
30%	0.30	3/10
25%	0.25	1/4, 2/8
20%	0.20	1/5
	0.16̄	1/6
15%	0.15	
	0.125	1/8
10%	0.10	1/10
5%	0.05	1/20
0%	0.01 / 0.00	0 1/100

IMPOSSIBLE

VERY LIKELY · LIKELY · UNLIKELY · VERY UNLIKELY · EXTREMELY UNLIKELY

SRB 122–123

Multiplication of Whole Numbers and Decimals Study Link 2.8

For each problem:

- Make a magnitude estimate. Circle the appropriate box.

- Solve the problem. Show your work at the right.

1. 8 * 19 = _____

10s	100s	1,000s	10,000s

2. 155 * 6 = _____

10s	100s	1,000s	10,000s

3. 37 * 58 = _____

10s	100s	1,000s	10,000s

4. 5 * 4.2 = _____

0.1s	1s	10s	100s

5. 9.3 * 2.8 = _____

0.1s	1s	10s	100s

6. 11.3 * 0.2 = _____

0.1s	1s	10s	100s

Estimation

1. Use only estimation to answer the following questions.

   a. Certain varieties of sea horses can move 10.5 inches per minute. Would these sea horses be able to travel 6 yards in 1 hour?

   _____

   b. Orville Wright completed the first successful airplane flight on December 17, 1903. He traveled 120 feet in 12 seconds. If he had been able to stay in the air for a full minute, would he have traveled 1 mile? (*Hint:* 1 mile = 5,280 feet)

   _____

   c. In 1960, the *Triton* became the first submarine to circumnavigate the world. It covered 36,014 miles in 76 days. Is that more or less than 100 miles per day?

   _____

2. It is said that the Aztec king, Montezuma, drank about 50 cups of chocolate a day. Based on this information, answer the following questions.

   a. About how much did he drink per week? _____
   (unit)

   b. About how much per year? _____
   (unit)

   Source: The Kids' World Almanac of Records and Facts

Challenge

3. Use paper and pencil to solve the following problem.

   The second edition of the *Oxford English Dictionary* was published, in 20 volumes, in 1989. The dictionary contains about 2,436,600 quotations. There are more quotations from the works of Shakespeare than from any other author—about 33,300. There are about 487,200 from the twentieth century, about 755,300 from the nineteenth century, and about 268,000 from the eighteenth century. About how many quotations are there from before the eighteenth century?

   _____
   (unit)

Unit 3: Geometry Explorations and the American Tour

In Unit 3 your child will set out on the American Tour, a yearlong series of mathematical activities that will examine historical, demographic, and environmental features of the United States. The American Tour involves a wide range of mathematical skills, but most important, it seeks to develop your child's ability to read, interpret, critically examine, and use mathematical information presented in text, tables, and graphics. These skills are essential to effective mathematics in our technological age.

Many American Tour activities are based on materials in the American Tour section of the *Student Reference Book.* The American Tour, a cross between an historical atlas and an almanac, contains maps, data, and other information from a wide range of sources, including the U.S. Census Bureau, the National Weather Service, and the National Geographic Society.

Unit 3 also will review some geometry concepts from earlier grades, while introducing and expanding on others. In *Fourth Grade Everyday Mathematics,* students used a compass to construct basic shapes and create geometric designs. In this unit, your child will extend these skills and be introduced to the concept of congruent figures (same size, same shape) by using a compass and a straightedge to copy triangles. Another tool that will be introduced is the Geometry Template, which contains protractors and rulers for measuring, and cutouts for drawing a variety of geometric figures.

Finally, students will be introduced to the mathematics and art of tessellations—patterns of shapes that cover a surface without gaps or overlaps—and will begin to create their own designs.

You may wish to help your child at home by asking questions about information presented in newspaper and magazine tables and graphics. Also, the world is filled with many 2-dimensional and 3-dimensional geometric forms: angles, line segments, curves, cubes, cylinders, spheres, pyramids, and so on. Many wonderful geometric patterns can be seen in nature as well as in the things that people create. It will be helpful for you and your child to look for and talk about geometric shapes throughout the year.

Please keep this Family Letter for reference as your child works through Unit 3.

Vocabulary

Important terms in Unit 3:

acute angle An angle with a measure greater than 0 degrees and less than 90 degrees.

Acute angle

adjacent angles Angles that are next to each other; adjacent angles have a common side, but no other overlap. In the diagram, angles 1 and 2 are adjacent angles. So are angles 2 and 3, angles 3 and 4, and angles 4 and 1.

Adjacent angles

congruent Having exactly the same shape and size.

Congruent triangles

diameter A line segment that passes through the center of a circle (or sphere) and has endpoints on the circle (or sphere); also, the length of this line segment. The diameter of a circle or sphere is twice the length of its radius.

Diameter

equilateral triangle A triangle with all three sides the same length. In an equilateral triangle, all three angles have the same measure.

Equilateral triangles

obtuse angle An angle with a measure greater than 90 degrees and less than 180 degrees.

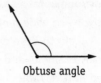

Obtuse angle

radius A line segment from the center of a circle (or sphere) to any point on the circle (or sphere); also, the length of this line segment.

Radius

right angle An angle with a measure of 90 degrees.

Right angle

tessellation An arrangement of shapes that covers a surface completely without overlaps or gaps. Also called *tiling*.

A tessellation

vertical (or opposite) angles When two lines intersect, the angles that do not share a common side. Vertical angles have equal measures. In the diagram, angles 2 and 4 are a pair of vertical angles. Angles 1 and 3 are another pair of vertical angles.

Vertical angles

Use with Lesson 2.11.

Building Skills through Games

In Unit 3, your child will practice geometry skills by playing the following games. For detailed instructions, see the *Student Reference Book.*

Angle Tangle See *Student Reference Book,* page 258
Two players will need a protractor and a straightedge to play this game. Playing *Angle Tangle* gives students practice in drawing and measuring angles.

Polygon Capture See *Student Reference Book,* page 289
This game uses 16 polygons and 16 Property Cards, and is played by partners or 2 teams each with 2 players. *Polygon Capture* gives students practice in identifying properties of polygons related to sides and angles.

Do-Anytime Activities

To work with your child on the concepts taught in this unit and in previous units, try these interesting and rewarding activities:

1 Together, read the book *A Cloak for the Dreamer* by Marilyn Burns.

2 When you are at home or at a store, ask your child to identify different types of polygons such as triangles, squares, pentagons, and hexagons.

3 Visit the Web site for the U.S. Bureau of the Census at http://www.census.gov/. Have your child write three interesting pieces of information that he or she learned from the Web site.

4 Look for examples of bar graphs in newspapers or magazines. Ask your child to explain the information shown by a graph.

As You Help Your Child with Homework

As your child brings assignments home, you may want to go over the instructions together, clarifying them as necessary. The answers listed below and on the next page will guide you through this unit's Study Links.

Study Link 3.1

1. Sample answer: The more years of school completed, the higher the median income.

2. Answers vary.

3. Answers vary.

Study Link 3.2

1. Look before you leap.   **2.** 5,472,000

3. Saying H   **4.** Answers vary.

5. Answer vary; Sample answer: The numbers are from a sample, not a census. They have been rounded to the nearest 1,000.

6. a. 250,000,000   **b.** 55%

Study Link 3.3

1. 60°; 90°; 60°   **2.** 120°; 60°; 60°

3. 90°; 135°; 135° **4.** 30°; 75°

Study Link 3.4

1. 70°   **2.** 50°   **3.** 110°   **4.** 130°

5. 60°   **6.** 180°   **7.** 120°   **8.** 90°

9. 50°   **10.** 150°   **11.** 170°   **12.** 260°

Study Link 3.5

1. acute; 12°

2. acute; 65°

3. obtuse; 103°

4. Sample answer: Angle *D* and angle *E*

5. Sample answer: Angle *D* and angle *F*

6. Sample answer: Angle *D* and angle *F*

7. a. 110°

b. Angle *F* and angle *D* are vertical (or opposite) angles; vertical angles are equal in measure.

Study Link 3.6

1. scalene   **2.** isosceles

3. isosceles; right   **4.** equilateral; isosceles

5. Objects and types of angles vary.   **6.** 60°; 60°; 60°

7. Sample answer: 6 angles with the same measure as ∠*A* fit around a point. Since a circle has 360°, and the angles in an equilateral triangle are equal, each angle measures 360 / 6, or 60°.

Study Link 3.7

Sample answers are given for Problems 1–5.

1.   The pentagon is the only shape that is not regular.

2.   The chevron is the only shape that is not convex.

3.  The oval is the only shape that is curved.

4.   This shape is the only one that is not convex.

5.   The trapezoid is the only shape without two pairs of parallel sides.

Study Link 3.8

1.–3. Samples of tessellations vary.

Study Link 3.9

1. Sample answer: Draw a line between two of the vertices to create two triangles. Since the sum of the angles in each triangle is 180°, the sum of the angles in a quadrangle is 360°.

2. 360°

3. a.–b.    **c.–d.**

Study Link 3.10

1. Sample answers are given.

a. 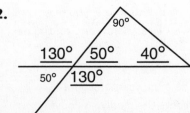 **b.**   **c.**   **d.**

2.

90°

130° 50° 40°

50° 130°

3. a. 2   **b.** 70°   **c.** 360°   **d.** trapezoid

Education and Earnings

The table below contains information from surveys by the U.S. Census Bureau. The information describes Householders who were at least 25 years old. A *Householder* is the person in whose name a home is owned or rented. If a house is owned jointly by a husband and wife, the Householder could be either the husband or the wife.

Years of School Completed	1990			1980		
	Number of Householders (thousands)	Percent of House-holders	Median Income	Number of House-holders (thousands)	Percent of House-holders	Median Income
Elementary (less than 9 years)	10,146	11%	$13,523	14,012	18%	$ 8,875
High School (1–3 years)	10,007	11%	$18,191	10,547	14%	$13,213
High School (4 years)	32,043	36%	$28,744	25,454	34%	$19,638
College (1–3 years)	16,451	19%	$35,724	11,480	15%	$21,740
College (4 years)	11,443	13%	$47,083	7,862	10%	$27,339
College (5 or more years)	9,269	10%	$54,636	6,661	9%	$30,684
Total	89,359	100%	$30,757	76,016	100%	$18,383

Source: March Current Population Survey, prepared by Income Statistics Branch/HHES Division U.S. Bureau of the Census

Use the table to answer the following questions.

1. Describe the relationship between number of years of education and income.

_____

_____

2. In which year do you think a higher percentage of Householders were high school graduates—1990 or 2000? Explain your answer.

_____

_____

_____

3. On the back of this page, write one question that can be answered using the information in the table.

An Unofficial Census

In 1991, author Tom Heymann took an unofficial U.S. census. The table shows how many people believed various common sayings, based on the sample of the population that he surveyed.

	Saying	Number Who Believe Saying Is True
A	Look before you leap.	175,104,000
B	The grass is always greener on the other side of the fence.	69,312,000
C	Haste makes waste.	153,216,000
D	Beauty is only skin deep.	149,568,000
E	Don't cry over spilled milk.	160,512,000
F	The early bird catches the worm.	136,800,000
G	A penny saved is a penny earned.	155,040,000
H	Don't count your chickens before they hatch.	169,632,000

Source: *The Unofficial U.S. Census* by Tom Heymann. Ballantine Books, 1991

1. Which saying had the largest number of believers?

_____

2. How many more people believed Saying E than Saying G? _____

3. Which saying had about 100 million more believers than Saying B? _____

4. Choose one of the expressions and tell what it means in your own words.

_____

5. Why do you think the numbers in the table all have zeros in the ones, tens,

and hundreds place? _____

_____

Challenge

6. a. About $\frac{7}{10}$ of the U.S. population in 1991 believed
Saying A to be true. What was the total population? _____

b. About what percent of the total population believed Saying F to
be true? (Use your calculator. Round to the nearest whole percent.) _____

Finding Angle Measures

Figure out the angle measures for the labeled angles in the patterns below. Remember that there are 360° in a circle and 180° in a straight line. Use the Geometry Template or cut out the shapes at the bottom of this page to help you. Do not use a protractor.

1.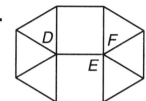

m∠D = _____°

m∠E = _____°

m∠F = _____°

2.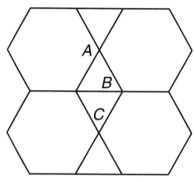

m∠A = _____°

m∠B = _____°

m∠C = _____°

3.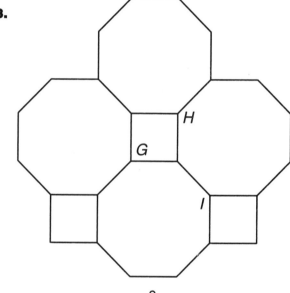

m∠G = _____°

m∠H = _____°

m∠I = _____°

On the back of this page, explain how you found the measure of ∠I.

Challenge

4.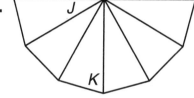

m∠J = _____°

m∠K = _____°

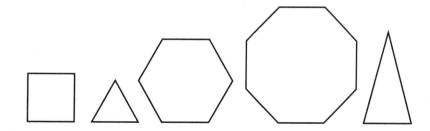

Angle Measures

Find the approximate measure of each angle at the right.

1. measure of ∠CAT = _____ °

2. m ∠BAR = _____ °

3. m ∠RAT = _____ °

4. m ∠CAB = _____ °

5. m ∠BAT = _____ °

6. m ∠CAR = _____ °

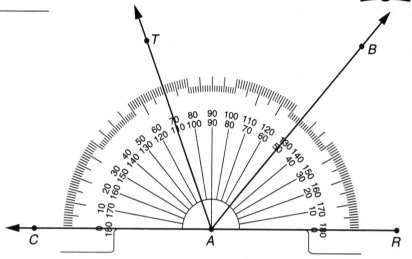

Find the approximate measure of each angle at the right.

7. m ∠MEN = _____ °

8. m ∠DEN = _____ °

9. m ∠MET = _____ °

10. m ∠MED = _____ °

11. m ∠TEN = _____ °

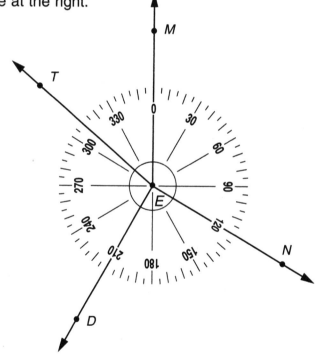

Challenge

12. measure of the reflex angle *TED* = _____ °

Circle *acute, right,* or *obtuse* for each angle in triangle *ABC*.
Then measure each angle.

1. ∠*ABC*   acute   right   obtuse   m∠*ABC* = _____°

2. ∠*CAB*   acute   right   obtuse   m∠*CAB* = _____°

3. ∠*BCA*   acute   right   obtuse   m∠*BCA* = _____°

Use the figure at the right to do Problems 4–6.

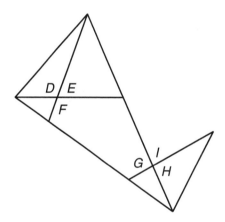

4. Name a pair of adjacent angles.

_____ and _____

5. Name a pair of vertical angles.

_____ and _____

6. Name a pair of opposite angles.

_____ and _____

Challenge

7. a. The measure of ∠*F* is 110°. What is the measure of ∠*D*? _____°

b. Explain how you know.

_____

_____

Triangle and Angle Review

For each triangle below, fill in the ovals for all of the names that apply.

1.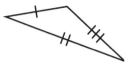

2.

3.

4.

O equilateral	O equilateral	O equilateral	O equilateral
O isosceles	O isosceles	O isosceles	O isosceles
O right	O right	O right	O right
O scalene	O scalene	O scalene	O scalene

5. On the back of this page, draw three angles of different sizes that you find at home. (For example, you could trace one corner of a book.) For each angle, name the object that has the angle. Then use words from the Word Bank to name each angle.

    a. Object _____

       Type of angle _____

    b. Object _____

       Type of angle _____

    c. Object _____

       Type of angle _____

Word Bank		
acute	obtuse	right
adjacent	reflex	straight

Challenge

6. Use what you know about equilateral triangles and the degree measure of a circle or a straight angle. What is the measure of each angle in equilateral triangle *ABC*?

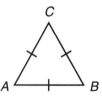

    m∠*A* = _____°   m∠*B* = _____°   m∠*C* = _____°

7. Explain how you found your answer to Problem 6. _____

_____

_____

_____

Odd Shape Out

In each set of shapes, there is one shape that doesn't belong. Cross out that shape and tell why it doesn't belong. (There may be more than one possible reason. What's important is having a good reason for crossing out a shape.)

1.

Reason: _____

_____

2.

Reason: _____

_____

3.

Reason: _____

_____

4.

Reason: _____

_____

5.

Reason: _____

_____

6. Make up your own "Odd Shape Out" problem on the back of this page. Ask a friend or family member to solve it.

Tessellation Museum

A **tessellation** is an arrangement of repeated, closed shapes that completely cover a surface, without overlaps or gaps. Sometimes only one shape is used in a tessellation. Sometimes two or more shapes are used.

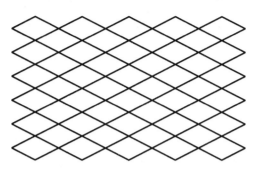

1. Collect tessellations. Look in newspapers and magazines. Ask people at home to help you find examples.

2. Ask an adult if you may cut out the tessellations. Tape your tessellations onto this page in the space below.

3. If you can't find tessellations in newspapers or magazines, look around your home at furniture, wallpaper, tablecloths, or clothing. In the space below, sketch the tessellations you find.

Sums of Angle Measures

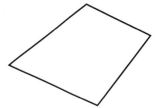

1. Describe one way to find the sum of the angles in a quadrangle without using a protractor. You may want to use the quadrangle at the right to illustrate your explanation.

_____

_____

_____

_____

_____

2. The sum of the angles in a quadrangle is _____ °.

3. Do the following to check your answer to Problem 2.

    a. With a straightedge, draw a large quadrangle on a separate sheet of paper.

    b. Draw an arc in each angle.

    c. Cut out the quadrangle and tear off part of each angle.

    d. Tape or glue the angles onto the back of this page so that the angles touch but do not overlap.

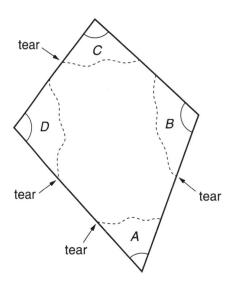

Polygons and Their Measures

1. Draw each of the following figures.

   a. a polygon

   b. a triangle with
      no equal sides

   c. a quadrangle
      with one right
      angle

   d. a quadrangle
      with no pairs
      of parallel sides

2. Without using a protractor, record the missing angle measurements in the
   figure below.

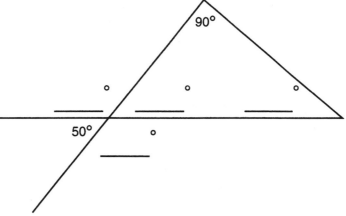

3. Use the figure below to answer the following questions.

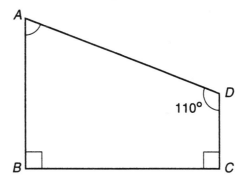

   a. How long is line segment *CD*? _____ cm

   b. What is the measure of angle *A*? _____

   c. What is the sum of the measures of all the angles? _____

   d. What is a geometric name for the figure? _____

Family Letter

Unit 4: Division

Unit 4 begins with a review of division facts and the relation between division and multiplication. Emphasis is on fact families—a person who knows that 4 * 5 = 20 also knows the related facts 5 * 4 = 20, 20 ÷ 4 = 5, and 20 ÷ 5 = 4.

We will develop strategies for dividing mentally. Challenge your child to a game of *Division Dash* to assist in practicing mental division. Rules are in the *Student Reference Book,* page 267.

These notations for division are equivalent:	
$12\overline{)246}$	$246 \div 12$
246 / 12	$\dfrac{246}{12}$

In *Fourth Grade Everyday Mathematics,* students were introduced to a method of long division called the partial-quotients division algorithm. This algorithm is easier to learn and apply than the traditional long division method. It relies on "easy" multiplication, and it can be quickly employed by students who struggle with traditional computation.

In this method, a series of partial answers (partial quotients) are obtained, and then added to get the final answer (the quotient). After your child has worked with this method, you might ask him or her to explain the example below:

$$
\begin{array}{r|l}
12\overline{)158} & \\
-\ 120 & 10 \\
\hline
38 & \\
-\ \ 36 & 3 \\
\hline
2 & 13
\end{array}
$$

Remainder   Quotient

In the coming unit, we will review the partial-quotients division algorithm and extend it to decimals.

Your child will have many opportunities to practice using this division algorithm—as well as others, if he or she wishes. The partial-quotients division algorithm, and another method called column division, are described in the *Student Reference Book.*

When we solve division number stories, special attention will be placed on interpreting the remainder in division.

The American Tour will continue as the class measures distances on maps and uses map scales to convert the map distances to real-world distances between cities, lengths of rivers, and so on.

Please keep this Family Letter for reference as your child works through Unit 4.

Vocabulary

Important terms in Unit 4:

dividend In division, the number that is being divided. For example, in $35 \div 5 = 7$, the dividend is 35.

division Division is used to find how a total can be separated into a number of groups, or into groups of equal size.

divisor In division, the number that divides another number. For example, in $35 \div 5 = 7$, the divisor is 5.

magnitude estimate A very rough estimate. A magnitude estimate tells whether an answer should be in the tens, hundreds, thousands, millions, and so on.

map legend or key A diagram that explains the symbols, markings, and colors on a map.

map scale A tool that helps you estimate real distances between places shown on a map by relating distances on the map to distances in the real world. For example, a map scale may show that one inch on a map represents 100 miles in the real world.

number sentence A sentence made up of at least two numbers or expressions and a single relation symbol $(=, <, >, \neq, \leq, \text{ or } \geq)$. For example, $5 + 5 = 10$ is a number sentence. Number sentences usually contain at least one operation symbol. They may also have grouping symbols, such as parentheses. If a number sentence contains one or more variables, it is called an *open sentence*.

open sentence A *number sentence* in which one or more *variables* hold the places of missing numbers. For example, $x + 3 = 5$ is an open sentence.

quotient The result of dividing one number by another number. For example, in $35 \div 5 = 7$, the quotient is 7.

remainder The amount left over when dividing one number by another number. For example, if 38 books are divided into 5 equal piles, there will be 7 books in each pile, with 3 books left over; the remainder is 3. We may write $38 \div 5 \rightarrow 7 \text{ R3}$, where R3 stands for the remainder.

variable A letter or other symbol that represents a number. A variable can represent one specific number or it can stand for many different numbers.

Do-Anytime Activities

To work with your child on the concepts taught in this unit and in previous units, try these interesting and rewarding activities:

1 Provide your child with opportunities to look at maps from various parts of the country. Ask him or her to explain the map legend and map scale, and to find the distances between two cities or places of interest.

2 Read the book *A Remainder of One* by Elinor J. Pinczes.

3 Play *Division Dash, First to 100,* or *Algebra Election* as described in the *Student Reference Book.*

4 Ask your child to write number stories that can be solved using division. Help your child solve those problems, and then identify how the quotient and remainder are used to answer the question in the number story.

Building Skills through Games

In Unit 4, your child will practice division as well as other skills by playing the following games. For detailed instructions, see the *Student Reference Book.*

Division Dash
See *Student Reference Book,* page 267
This is a game for one or two players. Each player will need a calculator. Playing *Division Dash* helps students practice division and mental calculation.

First to 100
See *Student Reference Book,* page 273
This is a game for two to four players and requires 32 Problem Cards and a pair of six-sided dice. Players answer questions after substituting numbers for the variable on Problem Cards. The questions offer practice on a variety of mathematical topics.

Algebra Election
See *Student Reference Book,* pages 256 and 257
This game is similar to *First to 100,* and uses the same 32 Problem Cards. Players will also need several pennies, 1 six-sided die, a calculator, and a gameboard called the Electoral Vote Map. The game rules model election of a president by winning sufficient electoral votes.

As You Help Your Child with Homework

As your child brings assignments home, you may want to go over the instructions together, clarifying them as necessary. The answers listed below will guide you through this unit's Study Links.

Study Link 4.1

1. 5 times taller

2. 50 students

3. 8 hours

4. 2 gallons

5. 2,000 miles

6. 3 weeks

7. 5 pounds

Study Link 4.2

1. 71

2. 53

3. 82 R22

4. 83

Study Link 4.3

1. **a.** About 1 mile   **b.** About $1\frac{1}{2}$ miles

2. **a.** Snakey Lane   **b.** About 2 miles

3. About $4\frac{1}{2}$ miles

4.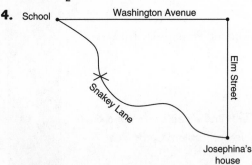

Sample answer: Since Josephina's father was walking twice as fast as Josephina, I marked a spot so that the distance from Josephina's house to the X was twice as long as the distance between school and the X.

Study Link 4.4

Estimates vary. Sample estimates are given for Problems 1–6.

1. The 10s box should be circled; $60 \div 6 = 10$; 13.1

2. The 100s box should be circled; $300 \div 3 = 100$; 129

3. The 1s box should be circled; $30 \div 10 = 3$; $3.69

4. The 10s box should be circled; $800 \div 40 = 20$; 23

5. The 100s box should be circled; $1,000 \div 5 = 200$; 169

6. The 1s should be circled; $18 \div 9 = 2$; 1.76

Study Link 4.5

1. $6.25; Reported it as a fraction or decimal; Sample answer: $50.00 divided by 8 games is $6.00 per game with $2.00 left over. $2.00 divided by 8 games is $0.25 per game. $6.00 + $0.25 = $6.25

2. 7; Ignored it; Sample answer: 7 pizzas cost $56.00. The remaining $4.00 is not enough to buy another pizza, and is ignored.

Study Link 4.6

1. 49   **2.** 780   **3.** 610

Answers vary for Problems 4–11.

Use with Lesson 3.11.

Uses of Division

Use what you know about division facts to solve the following problems. (Think: *How many of these are in that?*) Include units in your answers when appropriate.

1. Fifteen-year-old oak trees are often about 25 feet tall. Rose, a 15-year-old girl, is about 5 feet tall. How many times taller are the trees than Rose? _____

2. The job of interviewing 500 students in a school is to be divided equally among 10 interviewers. How many students should each interviewer talk to? _____

3. At an average speed of 50 miles per hour, about how long will a 400-mile trip take? _____

4. A summer camp serves 180 gallons of milk per month to 90 campers. About how much milk, on average, does each camper drink per month? _____

5. The diameter of Earth is about 4 times the diameter of the Moon. Earth's diameter is about 8,000 miles. What is the approximate diameter of the Moon? _____

8,000 miles

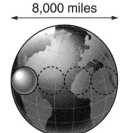

Challenge

Problems 6 and 7 were given to eighth graders on a test used to measure the progress of students in the United States. See how well you can do.

6. Jill needs to earn $45 for a class trip. She earns $2 each day on Mondays, Tuesdays, and Wednesdays. She earns $3 each day on Thursdays, Fridays, and Saturdays. She does not work on Sundays. How many weeks will it take her to earn $45? _____

7. The weight of an object on the Moon would be $\frac{1}{6}$ of its weight on Earth. An object that weighs 30 pounds on Earth would weigh how many pounds on the Moon? _____

> Problem 6 was solved correctly by 59% of the eighth graders who tried it. Problem 7 was solved correctly by 49%.

Division

Here is an example of division using the partial-quotients algorithm.

```
8)185
 - 80    10
  105
 - 80    10
   25
 - 24     3
    1    23
    ↑     ↑
```
Remainder Quotient

How many 8s are in 185? At least 10.
The first partial quotient. 10 * 8 = 80
Subtract. At least 10 [8s] are left.
The second partial quotient. 10 * 8 = 80
Subtract. At least 3 [8s] are left.
The third partial quotient. 3 * 8 = 24
Subtract. Add partial quotients: 10 + 10 + 3 = 23

Answer: 23 R1

Solve.

1. 639 ÷ 9   Answer: _____

2. 954 ÷ 18   Answer: _____

3. 1,990 / 24 Answer: _____

4. Robert is making a photo album. 6 photos fit on a page. How many pages

will he need for 497 photos? _____ pages

Distance to School

There are two ways to go from Josephina's house to school. She can take Elm Street and then Washington Avenue. She can also take Snakey Lane.

Use the map and scale below to answer the questions.

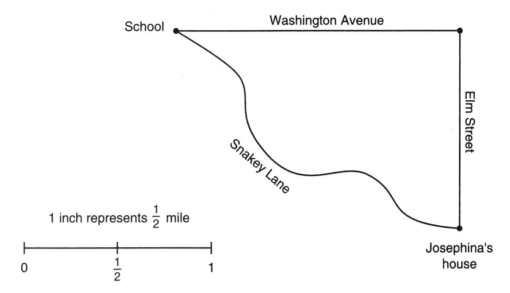

1 inch represents $\frac{1}{2}$ mile

1. Josephina started walking from home to school along Elm Street.

   a. How far would Josephina walk before she turned onto Washington Avenue? _____

   b. How far would she be from school when she turned the corner? _____

2. a. If Josephina wanted to take the shortest route to school, which road(s) should she take? _____

   b. What is this distance? _____

3. Josephina's father jogged from home to the school along Snakey Lane. He jogged back home along Washington Avenue and Elm Street. About how far did he jog in all? _____

4. Josephina left school and walked down Snakey Lane. Her father left home at the same time and walked up Snakey Lane. If her father was walking twice as fast as Josephina, where did they meet? Put a mark on the road where they met. On the back of this page, explain how you found your answer.

Estimate and Calculate Quotients

For each problem:

- Make a magnitude estimate of the quotient. Ask yourself: *Is the answer in the tenths, ones, tens, or hundreds?*

- Circle a box to show the magnitude of your estimate.

- Write a number sentence to show how you estimated.

- If there is a decimal point, ignore it. Divide the numbers.

- Use your magnitude estimate to place the decimal point in the final answer.

1. $6\overline{)78.6}$

0.1s	1s	10s	100s

How I estimated: _____

Answer: _____

2. $3\overline{)387}$

0.1s	1s	10s	100s

How I estimated: _____

Answer: _____

3. $29.52 \div 8$

0.1s	1s	10s	100s

How I estimated: _____

Answer: _____

4. $989 \div 43$

0.1s	1s	10s	100s

How I estimated: _____

Answer: _____

5. 845 / 5

0.1s	1s	10s	100s

How I estimated: _____

Answer: _____

6. 15.84 / 9

0.1s	1s	10s	100s

How I estimated: _____

Answer: _____

Division Number Stories with Remainders   Study Link 4.5

For each number story:
- Draw a picture and write a number sentence if you want.
- Use a division algorithm to solve the problem.
- Decide what to do about the remainder.
- Explain why you treated the remainder the way you did.

Example

You need to set up benches for a play. Each bench can seat 7 people. You expect 66 people to attend. How many benches do you need?

_10_ benches

What did you do about the remainder? Circle the answer.

Ignored it.   Reported it as a fraction or decimal.   (Rounded the answer up.)

Why? _9 benches seat 63 people. One more bench is needed for 3 remaining people._

---

1. It costs $50.00 to be a member of a soccer team. The team plays 8 games during the season. What is the cost per game?

$_____

What did you do about the remainder? Circle the answer.

Ignored it.   Reported it as a fraction or decimal.   Rounded the answer up.

Why? _____

_____

2. Lynn is having a party. Pizzas cost $8.00 each. How many pizzas can she buy with $60.00?

_____ pizzas

What did you do about the remainder? Circle the answer.

Ignored it.   Reported it as a fraction or decimal.   Rounded the answer up.

Why? _____

_____

Variables

For Problems 1–3:

- Find the value of x in the first number sentence.
- Use this value to complete the second number sentence.

1. x = number of days in a week

$x^2 =$ _____

2. $x = \frac{1}{10}$ of 100

$x * 78 =$ _____

3. x = largest sum possible with 2 six-sided dice

$598 + x =$ _____

4. Count the number of letters in your first name and in your last name.

a. My first name has _____ letters. **b.** My last name has _____ letters.

c. Find the product of these 2 numbers. Product = _____.

Answer the questions in Problems 5–11 by replacing x with the product you found in Problem 4.

5. Is x a prime or a composite number? _____

6. Is $\frac{x}{30}$ less than 1? _____

7. Which is larger: $3 * x$ or $x + 100$? _____

8. What is the median and the range for
this set of 3 weights: 30 pounds, 52 pounds, x pounds? _____

9. There are 200 students at Henry Clissold School.
x% speak Spanish. How many students speak Spanish? _____

10. $(3x + 5) - 7 =$ _____

11. True or false: $x^2 > 30 * x$ _____

Unit 5: Fractions, Decimals, and Percents

The focus of Unit 5 will be on naming numbers as fractions, decimals, and percents. Your child will use pattern blocks to review basic fraction and mixed-number concepts and notations, and will formulate rules for finding equivalent fractions.

In *Fourth Grade Everyday Mathematics*, your child learned to convert easy fractions, such as $\frac{1}{2}$, $\frac{1}{4}$, $\frac{1}{10}$, and $\frac{3}{4}$, to equivalent decimals and percents. For example, $\frac{1}{2}$ can be renamed as 0.5 and as 50%. Your child will now learn (with the help of a calculator) how to rename any fraction as a decimal and as a percent.

In this unit, *Everyday Mathematics* introduces two new games: *Estimation Squeeze*, to practice estimating products; and *Frac-Tac-Toe*, to practice converting fractions to decimals and percents. These games, like others introduced earlier, are used to reduce the tedium that often comes with the drill of arithmetic skills. Your child will look forward to playing these games. Both games use simple materials (calculator, number cards, and pennies or other counters) so that you can play them at home.

Your child will explore historical data about the United States as the American Tour continues. The class will study education information from the past and compare it with current information.

Please keep this Family Letter for reference as your child works through Unit 5.

Vocabulary

Important terms in Unit 5:

bar graph A graph that uses horizontal or vertical bars to represent data.

circle graph A graph in which a circle and its interior are divided into parts to show the parts of a set of data. The whole circle represents the whole set of data.

denominator The number below the line in a fraction. In a fraction where a whole is divided into equal parts, the denominator represents the number of equal parts into which the whole (the ONE or unit) is divided. In the fraction $\frac{a}{b}$, b is the denominator.

equivalent fractions Fractions that have different denominators but name the same amount. For example, $\frac{1}{2}$ and $\frac{4}{8}$ are equivalent fractions.

improper fraction A fraction whose numerator is greater than or equal to its denominator. For example, $\frac{4}{3}, \frac{5}{2}, \frac{4}{4},$ and $\frac{24}{12}$ are improper fractions. In *Everyday Mathematics*, improper fractions are sometimes called "top-heavy" fractions.

mixed number A number that is written using both a whole number and a fraction. For example, $2\frac{1}{4}$ is a mixed number equal to $2 + \frac{1}{4}$.

numerator The number above the line in a fraction. In a fraction where the whole is divided into a number of equal parts, the numerator represents the number of equal parts that are being considered. In the fraction $\frac{a}{b}$, a is the numerator.

percent (%) Per hundred, or out of a hundred. For example, "48% of the students in the school are boys" means that 48 out of every 100 students in the school are boys.

Percent Circle A tool on the Geometry Template that is used to measure or draw figures that involve percents (such as circle graphs).

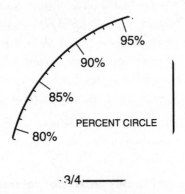

repeating decimal A decimal in which one digit or a group of digits is repeated without end. For example, 0.333... and $0.\overline{147}$ are repeating decimals.

Use with Lesson 4.7.

Do-Anytime Activities

To work with your child on the concepts taught in this unit and in previous units, try these interesting and rewarding activities:

1 Help your child find fractions, decimals, and percents in the everyday world—in newspaper advertisements, on measuring tools, in recipes, in the sports section of the newspaper, and so on.

2 Over a period of time, have your child record daily temperatures in the morning and in the evening; and keep track of the temperatures in a chart. Then have your child make a graph from the data. Ask questions about the data. For example, have your child find the differences in temperatures from morning to evening or from one day to the next.

3 Practice using percents in the context of tips. For example, have your child calculate $\frac{1}{10}$ or 10% of amounts of money. Invite your child to find the tip the next time the family goes out for dinner.

4 Ask your child to identify 2-dimensional and 3-dimensional shapes around the house.

Building Skills through Games

In Unit 5, your child will practice operations and computation skills by playing the following games. For detailed instructions, see the *Student Reference Book*.

Multiplication Bull's-Eye See *Student Reference Book*, page 284
Two players use 4 each of the number cards 0–9, a six-sided die, and a calculator to play.
This game provides practice in estimating products.

Estimation Squeeze See *Student Reference Book*, page 268
This is a game for two players who use a single calculator. The game provides practice in estimating products.

Frac-Tac-Toe See *Student Reference Book*, pages 274–276
This is a game for two players. Game materials include 4 each of the number cards 0-10, pennies or counters of two colors, a calculator, and a gameboard. The gameboard is a 5-by-5 number grid that resembles a bingo card. Several versions of the gameboard are shown in the *Student Reference Book*. *Frac-Tac-Toe* helps students practice converting fractions to decimals and percents.

Fraction/Percent Concentration See *Student Reference Book*, page 278
This game provides help in memorizing some of the easy fraction/percent equivalencies.
Two or three players use 1 set of *Fraction/Percent Concentration* Tiles and a calculator to play.

As You Help Your Child with Homework

As your child brings assignments home, you may want to go over the instructions together, clarifying them as necessary. The answers listed below will guide you through this unit's Study Links.

Study Link 5.1

1. 9 **2.** 14 **3.** $\frac{4}{5}$

4. $\frac{9}{10}$ **5.** 70 **6.** 16

7. a. 9

    b. Sample answer: They have $\frac{3}{8}$ of the distance left to ride. $\frac{1}{8}$ of 24 miles is 3 miles. So $\frac{3}{8}$ of 24 miles is $3 * 3 = 9$ miles.

8. a. $9 **b.** $15

Study Link 5.2

3. $2\frac{1}{2}$; $\frac{5}{2}$ **4.** $2\frac{4}{6}$, or $2\frac{2}{3}$; $\frac{16}{6}$, or $\frac{8}{3}$

5. $1\frac{2}{3}$; $\frac{5}{3}$ **6.** $2\frac{1}{6}$; $\frac{13}{6}$

7. $2\frac{5}{6}$; $\frac{17}{6}$ **8.** Answers vary.

Study Link 5.3

1. 4 **2.** 12 **3.** 1; 4

4. $\frac{4}{4} = 1$ **5.** $\frac{6}{8} = \frac{3}{4}$ **6.** $\frac{5}{4} = 1\frac{1}{4}$

7. $\frac{9}{8}$, or $1\frac{1}{8}$ cups **8.** $\frac{7}{8}$ inch **9.** Answers vary.

Study Link 5.4

1. $\frac{6}{10}$ **2.** $\frac{15}{18}$ **3.** = **4.** no **5.** no

6. = **7.** = **8.** = **9.** = **10.** no

11. = **12.** no **13.** 6 **14.** 4 **15.** 12

16. 21 **17.** 40 **18.** 2

Study Link 5.5

1. 0.4 **2.** 1.9 **3.** 20.7 **4.** 24.0

5. 60.9 **6.** 160.6 **7.** 181.3 **8.** 296.4

9. 297.9 **10.** 316.0

Study Link 5.6

1. $\frac{7}{10}$; $1\frac{1}{10}$; $2\frac{3}{10}$; $4\frac{9}{10}$

2. 9.5

3. a. $\frac{15}{45}$, or $\frac{1}{3}$ **b.** $0.\overline{3}$ **c.** $\frac{9}{45}$, or $\frac{1}{5}$

    d. 0.2 **e.** $\frac{3}{45}$, or $\frac{1}{15}$ **f.** $0.0\overline{6}$

Study Link 5.7

1. a. 2 **b.** 8 **c.** $\frac{2}{8}$, or $\frac{1}{4}$

2. a. 6 **b.** 18 **c.** $\frac{6}{18}$, or $\frac{1}{3}$ **d.** $0.\overline{3}$

3. a. 4 **b.** $\frac{4}{9}$ **c.** $0.\overline{4}$

4. a. 6 **b.** $\frac{6}{22}$, or $\frac{3}{11}$ **c.** $0.\overline{27}$ or 0.27

Study Link 5.8

1. $\frac{3}{4} = 0.75 = 75\%$; $\frac{14}{16} = 0.875 = 88\%$; $\frac{15}{25} = 0.6 = 60\%$; $\frac{17}{20} = 0.85 = 85\%$; $\frac{3}{8} = 0.375 = 38\%$

3. $\frac{3}{8}$; $\frac{15}{25}$; $\frac{3}{4}$; $\frac{17}{20}$; $\frac{14}{16}$

4. $130

5. 10

6. 4; If 80% is 16 words, then 10% is $\frac{1}{8}$ of 16 words, or 2 words. So 100% is $10 * 2$, or 20 words. The test had 20 words. Louis missed $20 - 16 = 4$ words.

7. $10,000

Study Link 5.9

2. The circle graph; Sample answer: Because percent means per 100, or out of 100, the graph shows $\frac{33}{100}$ chose blue. If 100 students were in the class, 33 of them would have chosen blue.

3. Bar graph

4. Line graph

Study Link 5.10

1. a. 50% **b.** 15% **c.** 35%

Study Link 5.11

Check your child's circle graph.

Study Link 5.12

1. Jan's recipe calls for $\frac{1}{2}$ cup of flour.

2. Melise scored 84% on her spelling test.

3. Renee had $0.65 left after buying lunch.

Fraction-Stick Problems

Shade the fraction sticks to help you find equivalent fractions.

1. $\frac{1}{2} = \frac{\square}{8}$

2. $\frac{3}{4} = \frac{\square}{16}$

3. $\frac{\square}{4} = \frac{2}{8} = \frac{\square}{16}$

Shade the fraction sticks to help you solve the addition problems.

4. $\frac{1}{4} + \frac{3}{4} =$ _____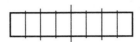

5. $\frac{1}{2} + \frac{2}{8} =$ _____

6. $\frac{1}{2} + \frac{3}{4} =$ _____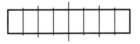

Shade the fraction sticks to help you solve the fraction number stories.

7. Joe was baking a cake. He added $\frac{3}{4}$ cup of white flour and $\frac{3}{8}$ cup of whole wheat flour. How much flour did he use in all?

_____
(unit)

8. Twanda glued together 2 wooden boards. One board was $\frac{3}{8}$-inch thick. The other was $\frac{1}{2}$-inch thick. How thick is the new board?

_____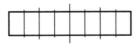
(unit)

9. On the back of this page, write a number story using fractions. Write a number model to show how you solved it.

Decimal Numbers

1. Mark each of these numbers on the number line. The first one is done for you.

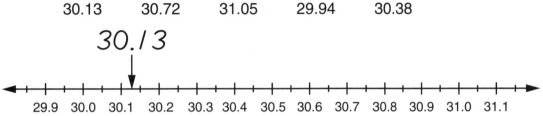

30.13   30.72   31.05   29.94   30.38

30.13

29.9   30.0   30.1   30.2   30.3   30.4   30.5   30.6   30.7   30.8   30.9   31.0   31.1

2. Below is a list of the 10 smallest countries in the world. Round the area of each country to the nearest tenth of a square kilometer.

Country	Area in Square Kilometers	Area Rounded to the Nearest Tenth of a Square Kilometer
1. Vatican City	0.44 km^2	_____ km^2
2. Monaco	1.89 km^2	_____ km^2
3. Nauru	20.72 km^2	_____ km^2
4. Tuvalu	23.96 km^2	_____ km^2
5. San Marino	60.87 km^2	_____ km^2
6. Liechtenstein	160.58 km^2	_____ km^2
7. Marshall Islands	181.30 km^2	_____ km^2
8. St. Kitts and Nevis	296.37 km^2	_____ km^2
9. Maldives	297.85 km^2	_____ km^2
10. Malta	315.98 km^2	_____ km^2

Source: Britannica Online

Just a Chip Off the Old Block

In area, the United States is the fourth-largest country in the world, covering about 9,373,000 square kilometers. Rhode Island, the smallest state in the United States, covers about 3,000 square kilometers.

Source: Statistical Abstracts of the United States

Decimals, Fractions, and Mixed Numbers

1. The five driest inhabited places in the world and the average amount of rain they each receive each year are listed below. Convert each decimal measurement to a fraction or a mixed number.

Location	Average Annual Rainfall Expressed as a Decimal	Average Annual Rainfall Expressed as a Fraction or a Mixed Number
Aswan, Egypt	0.5 mm	$\frac{1}{2}$ _____ mm
Luxor, Egypt	0.7 mm	_____ mm
Arica, Chile	1.1 mm	_____ mm
Ica, Peru	2.3 mm	_____ mm
Antofagasta, Chile	4.9 mm	_____ mm

Source: The Top 10 of Everything 2000

2. What is the total average annual rainfall for these 5 locations? _____ mm

3. America's longest place name is

    Chargoggagoggmanchauggagoggchaubunagungamaugg.

This name for a lake near Webster, Massachusetts, is 45 letters long. It is a Native American name that means, "You fish on your side, I'll fish on mine, and no one fishes in the middle." Use this word to answer the problems below.

a. What fraction of the word is made up of the letter *g*?   _____

b. Write the fraction from Part a as a decimal.   _____

c. What fraction of the word is made up of the letter *a*?   _____

d. Write the fraction from Part c as a decimal.   _____

e. What fraction of the word is made up of the letter *c*?   _____

f. Write the fraction from Part e as a decimal.   _____

Percent Problems

1. Convert the following fractions to decimals and percents. Round to the nearest whole percent.

Fraction	Decimal	Percent (rounded to the nearest whole percent)
$\frac{3}{4}$		
$\frac{14}{16}$		
$\frac{15}{25}$		
$\frac{17}{20}$		
$\frac{3}{8}$		

2. On the back of this page, explain how you could find the percent equivalent to $\frac{17}{20}$ without using a calculator.

3. Write the five fractions from Problem 1 in order from least to greatest.

_____   _____   _____   _____   _____

4. Katie spent 50% of her money on shoes for soccer. The shoes cost $65. How much money did Katie start with?   _____

5. Tom got 70% correct on a music test. If he got 7 questions correct, how many questions were on the test?   _____

6. Louis got 16 words correct on his vocabulary test. This was 80%. How many words did he miss?   _____

Explain how you got your answer. _____

_____

_____

Challenge

7. Lincoln School raised $3,000 for charity. This is 30% of the school's goal. What is Lincoln School's goal? _____

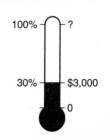

Graphs

Brenda's class made a list of their favorite colors. The results were as follows:

Blue 8   Red 7   Yellow 3   Green 2   Other 4

1. Circle each graph that correctly represents the data above. (There may be more than one.)

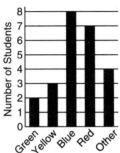
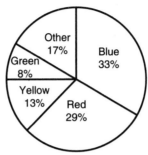
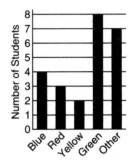

2. Which graph would help you answer the question "What fraction of the students chose blue as their favorite color?" _____

Explain. _____

_____

_____

Marsha kept track of the low temperatures at the end of May. They were as follows:

May 17	50°F	May 18	63°F	May 19	58°F	May 20	60°F
May 21	65°F	May 22	57°F	May 23	58°F	May 24	65°F
May 25	68°F	May 26	70°F	May 27	66°F	May 28	65°F
May 29	64°F	May 30	68°F	May 31	74°F		

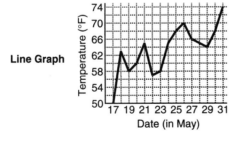
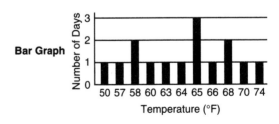

3. Which graph do you think is more helpful for answering the question "On how many days was the low temperature 65°F?" _____

4. Which graph do you think is more helpful for showing trends in the temperature for the last two weeks of May? _____

Circle Graphs and Collecting Data

Estimating the Size of Pieces in a Circle Graph

SRB
119 120

1. Estimate the percent of the circle for each piece of the graph at the right.

   a. A is about _____ of the circle.

   b. B is about _____ of the circle.

   c. C is about _____ of the circle.

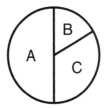

2. Draw a line connecting each data set with the most likely circle graph.

30% of Michel's class walks to school.	25% of Jeannene's toy cars are blue.	$\frac{1}{8}$ of Angelo's pants are jeans.
30% of Michel's class rides the bus.	10% of Jeannene's toy cars are striped.	$\frac{1}{8}$ of Angelo's pants are black dress pants.
40% of Michel's class rides in a car or van.	65% of Jeannene's toy cars are red.	$\frac{3}{4}$ of Angelo's pants are blue dress pants.

Challenge

3. Circle the graph above that you did not use. Write a set of data to match that circle graph.

_____

_____

Continue on the next page.

Circle Graphs and Collecting Data (cont.)

The Number of States We've Been In

4. Talk with an adult at home and think of all the states you have ever been in. (Be sure to include the state you're living in.) Look at the map below to help you remember.

Use a pencil or crayon to mark each state you have been in.

Don't count any state that you have flown over in an airplane, unless the plane landed and you left the airport.

5. Count the number of states you have marked.

I have been in _____ states in my lifetime.

6. Now ask the adult to mark the map to show the states he or she has been in, using a different color or mark from yours.

Keep a tally as states are marked.

The adult I interviewed has been in _____ states.

Note: Alaska and Hawaii are not shown to scale.

Student and adult: This data is important for our next mathematics class. Please bring this completed Study Link back to school tomorrow.

What's in a Landfill?

People who study landfills have estimated the percent of landfill space (volume) taken up by paper, food, plastic, and so on.

Space in landfills taken up by:

Paper 50%

Food and yard waste 13%

Plastic 10%

Metal 6%

Glass 1%

Other waste 20%

Think of it this way:
For every 100 boxes of garbage hauled to the dump, expect that about 50 boxes could be filled with paper, 6 with metal, 1 with glass, and so on.

Cut out the Percent Circle. Use it to make a circle graph for the data in the table. (Remember to label the graph and give it a title.)

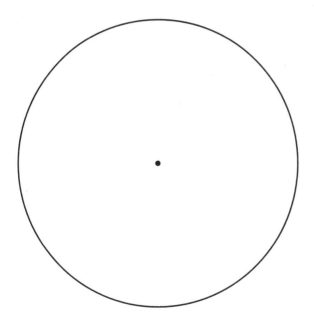

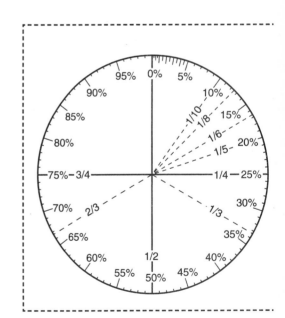

Fraction Review

Each statement below is expressed in an unusual way.
Rewrite it in the way such things are usually expressed.

Example The package weighed 200% of a pound.
            Rewrite as: The package weighed 2 pounds.

1. Jan's recipe calls for 50% of a cup of flour.

_____

2. Melise scored 0.84 on her spelling test.

_____

3. Renee had 65% of a dollar left after buying lunch.

_____

Fill in the tag on each name-collection box. Cross out the names that do not
belong and add 5 names of your own.

4.

$\frac{2}{4}$
$\frac{3}{8}$
0.5
100% − 50%
one-half

5.

$\frac{2}{3}$
one third less than 1
$\frac{5}{6}$
50%
0.23

Family Letter

Unit 6: Using Data; Addition and Subtraction of Fractions

The authors of *Everyday Mathematics* believe that students should do serious and substantial work with data. Unit 6 provides many activities designed to present and teach relevant data skills and concepts, allowing your child ample opportunities to practice organizing and analyzing the data he or she collects.

The data that your child initially collects will usually consist of an unorganized collection of numbers. After organizing the data using a variety of methods, he or she will study the **landmarks** of the data. The following terms are called landmarks because they show the important features of the data:

▷ The **maximum** is the largest data value observed.

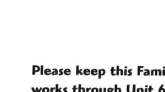

   ▷ The **minimum** is the smallest data value observed.

   ▷ The **range** is the difference between the maximum and the minimum.

   ▷ The **mode** is the "most popular" data value—the value observed most often.

   ▷ The **median** is the middle data value observed.

   ▷ The **mean,** commonly known as the "average," is a central value for a set of data.

At the end of the unit, students will have an opportunity to demonstrate their skills in this area by conducting a survey of their peers; gathering and organizing the data; analyzing their results; and writing a summary report.

Your child will continue his or her work with the American Tour by studying a variety of Native American measurements for length and distance based on parts of the body. Students will convert these body measures to personal measures by measuring their fingers, hands, and arms in both metric and U.S. customary units. In addition, your child will learn how to read a variety of contour-type maps, such as climate, precipitation, and growing-seasons maps.

Finally, students will explore addition and subtraction of fractions by using paper slide rules, the familiar clock face, and fraction sticks. They will learn to find common denominators and apply this skill in adding and subtracting fractions with unlike denominators.

Please keep this Family Letter for reference as your child works through Unit 6.

Vocabulary

Important terms in Unit 6:

angle of separation A measure of how far fingers can be spread apart. The figure shows the angle of separation between a person's thumb and first finger.

Angle of separation

common denominator Any number except zero that is a multiple of the denominators of two or more fractions. For example, the fractions $\frac{1}{2}$ and $\frac{2}{3}$ have common denominators 6, 12, 18, and so on.

contour line A curve on a map through places where a certain measurement (such as temperature or elevation) is the same. Often, contour lines separate regions that have been colored differently to show a range of conditions.

cubit An ancient unit of length, measured from the point of the elbow to the end of the middle finger. A cubit is about 18 inches.

decennial Occurring or being done every 10 years.

fair game A game in which each player has the same chance of winning. If any player has an advantage or disadvantage (for example, by playing first), then the game is not fair.

fathom A unit used by people who work with boats and ships to measure depths under water and lengths of cables. A fathom is now defined as 6 feet.

great span The distance from the tip of the thumb to the tip of the little finger (pinkie), when the hand is stretched as far as possible.

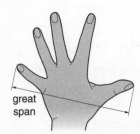

great span

landmark A notable feature of a data set. Landmarks include the *median, mode, maximum, minimum,* and *range.*

line plot A sketch of data in which check marks, Xs, or other marks above a number line show the frequency of each value.

map legend (map key) A diagram that explains the symbols, markings, and colors on a map.

maximum The largest amount; the greatest number in a set of data.

mean The sum of a set of numbers divided by the number of numbers in the set. The mean is often referred to simply as the **average.**

median The middle value in a set of data when the data are listed in order from smallest to largest. If there is an even number of data points, the median is the *mean* of the two middle values.

minimum The smallest amount; the smallest number in a set of data.

mode The value or values that occur most often in a set of data.

normal span The distance from the tip of the thumb to the tip of the first (index) finger of an outstretched hand. Also called *span.*

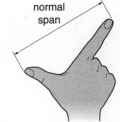

normal span

population In data collection, the collection of people or objects that is the focus of the study.

range The difference between the *maximum* and *minimum* in a set of data.

sample A part of a group chosen to represent the whole group.

simplest form A fraction less than 1 is in simplest form if there is no number other than 1 that divides its numerator and denominator evenly. A mixed number is in simplest form if its fractional part is in simplest form.

stem-and-leaf plot A display of data in which digits with larger place values are "stems" and digits with smaller place values are "leaves."

Stems (10s)	Leaves (1s)
2	4 4 5 6 7 7 8
3	1 1 2 2 6 6 6
4	1 1 3 5 8
5	0 2

Stem-and-leaf plot

survey A study that collects data.

Use with Lesson 5.13.

Do-Anytime Activities

To work with your child on the concepts taught in this unit and in previous units, try these interesting and rewarding activities:

1 Have your child design and conduct an informal survey. Help him or her collect and organize the data, and then describe the data using data landmarks. Challenge your child to create different ways in which the organized data can be presented.

2 Encourage your child to develop his or her own set of personal measures for both metric and U.S. customary units.

Building Skills through Games

In this unit, your child will work on his or her understanding of angles and the addition and subtraction of fractions by playing the following games. For detailed instructions, see the *Student Reference Book.*

Frac-Tac-Toe See *Student Reference Book*, pages 274–276
This is a game for two players. Game materials include 4 each of the number cards 0–10, pennies or counters of two colors, a calculator, and a gameboard. The gameboard is a 5-by-5 number grid that resembles a bingo card. Several versions of the gameboard are shown in the *Student Reference Book*. *Frac-Tac-Toe* helps students practice converting fractions to decimals and percents.

Angle Tangle See *Student Reference Book*, page 258
This is a game for two players and requires a protractor, a straight-edge, and paper. The game provides practice with measuring angles and estimating angle measures.

As You Help Your Child with Homework

As your child brings assignments home, you may want to go over the instructions together, clarifying them as necessary. The answers listed below will guide you through this unit's Study Links.

Study Link 6.1

3. a. 59 **b.** 24 **c.** 33
d. 36 **e.** 39.5

Study Link 6.2

1. a.–c. Answers vary.

2. a. cm; ft **b.** ounces; gal; liters
c. m; miles **d.** cm; ft; mm
e. kg; lb; grams

Study Link 6.3

1. 73 **2.** 19 **3.** 53

4. Sample answer: Cross off the highest and lowest values—31 and 73. Continue by crossing off the highest and lowest values remaining. Finally, only the number 53 remains. So 53 is the median.

Study Link 6.4

1. tapes and CDs

2. books and magazines

3. movie tickets

Study Link 6.5

Sample answers given for Problems 1–3.

1. 5, 7, 7, 8, 8, 9, 10, 13, 14, 15, 15, 15, 20

2.

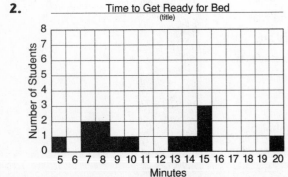

Time to Get Ready for Bed
(title)

3. The number of minutes it takes to get ready for bed

Study Link 6.6

1. Sample answer: The ages of the oldest people we know
Title: The Oldest People Our Class Knows
Unit: Years

2. a. 77 **b.** 94 **c.** 85 **d.** 85

3. Sample answer: Scores on a science test
Title: Science Test Scores
Unit: % Correct

4. a. 32 **b.** 99 **c.** 66 **d.** 78.5

Study Link 6.7

1. Florida; Arizona

2. Oregon; Washington

3. Answers vary.

4. Utah; Wyoming

Study Link 6.8

1. $\frac{12}{20}$, or $\frac{3}{5}$ **2.** $18\frac{1}{2}$; 9

3. 14; $1\frac{6}{8}$, or $1\frac{3}{4}$ **4.** 7; $\frac{7}{8}$

5. $\frac{7}{8}$ **6.** $2\frac{2}{8}$, or $2\frac{1}{4}$

Study Link 6.9

1. $\frac{22}{15}$, or $1\frac{7}{15}$ **2.** $\frac{1}{18}$

3. $\frac{9}{4}$, or $2\frac{1}{4}$ **4.** 4; $7\frac{3}{4}$

5. $5\frac{5}{6}$

Study Link 6.10

1. $\frac{18}{22} - \frac{11}{22} = \frac{7}{22}$ **2.** $\frac{20}{36} - \frac{9}{36} = \frac{11}{36}$

3. $\frac{21}{30} + \frac{8}{30} = \frac{29}{30}$ **4.** $\frac{21}{30} - \frac{8}{30} = \frac{13}{30}$

5. $\frac{19}{18}$, or $1\frac{1}{18}$ **6.** $\frac{59}{42}$, or $1\frac{17}{42}$

7. $\frac{1}{6}$ **8.** $\frac{3}{4}$

9. $\frac{2}{12}$, or $\frac{1}{6}$ **10.** $\frac{1}{2}$

11. $\frac{1}{3}$ **12.** $\frac{23}{12}$, or $1\frac{11}{12}$

13. $\frac{23}{12}$, or $1\frac{11}{12}$ **14.** $\frac{19}{12}$, or $1\frac{7}{12}$

The Standing Long Jump

Ms. Perez's physical education class participated in the standing long jump. Following are the results rounded to the nearest inch.

| 24 | 35 | 33 | 48 | 33 | 48 | 27 | 35 | 27 | 55 | 43 | 24 |
| 55 | 33 | 52 | 33 | 29 | 59 | 26 | 59 | 48 | 37 | 42 | 42 |

1. Organize these data on the line plot below.

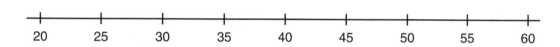

2. Make a bar graph for these data.

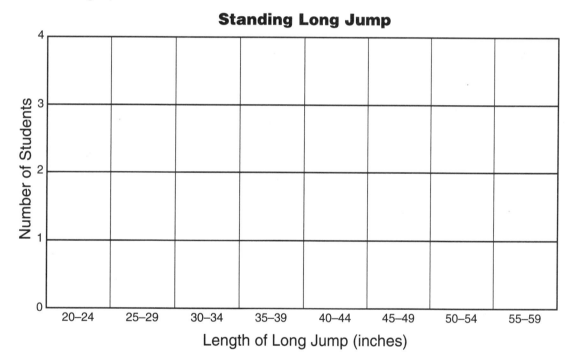

3. Find the following landmarks for the standing long jump data:

    a. Maximum (the longest distance a student jumped): _____ in.

    b. Minimum (the shortest distance a student jumped): _____ in.

    c. Mode: _____ in.   **d.** Median: _____ in.

    e. Mean (average): _____ in. (Use a calculator. Add the distances and divide the sum by the number of jumps. Round to the nearest tenth.)

Standard and Nonstandard Units

1. Use your body measures to find three objects that are about the size of each measurement below.

a. 1 cubit

b. 1 great span

c 1 finger width

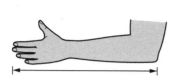

great span

_____   _____   _____

_____   _____   _____

_____   _____   _____

2. For each problem below, mark the unit or units you *could* use to measure the object.

a. Height of your ceiling   ◯ cm   ◯ ft   ◯ lb   ◯ miles

b. Amount of milk in a pitcher   ◯ cm   ◯ ounces   ◯ gal   ◯ liters

c. Depth of the ocean   ◯ m   ◯ ounces   ◯ gal   ◯ miles

d. Length of a bee   ◯ cm   ◯ ft   ◯ mm   ◯ liters

e. Weight of a nickel   ◯ in.   ◯ kg   ◯ lb   ◯ grams

Reading a Stem-and-Leaf Plot

Use the information below to answer the questions.

Randy was growing sunflowers. After eight weeks, he measured the height of his
sunflowers, in inches. He recorded the heights in the stem-and-leaf plot below.

Height of Sunflowers (inches)

Stems (10s)	Leaves (1s)
3	9 1
4	7 6 9 2 9
5	2 3 3 5 2 8 7 3
6	5 3 4
7	3

1. How tall is the tallest sunflower? _____ in.

   Which landmark is the height of the tallest flower? Circle its name.

   minimum   mode   maximum   mean

2. How many sunflowers did Randy measure? _____ sunflowers

3. What is the mode for his measurements? _____ in.

4. Explain how you would find the median for his measurements.

   _____

   _____

   _____

   _____

Challenge

5. On the back of this page, describe how Randy made his stem-and-leaf plot
   once he had his measurements.

How Much Do Students Spend?

Study Link 6.4

A fifth grade class collected data about how much students in the class spent per month on various items. Here are some of the results:

- A median amount of $6 per month was spent for books and magazines.

- A median amount of $10 per month was spent for tapes and CDs.

- A median amount of $8 per month was spent for movie tickets.

The number-line plots below display the data they collected. One plot shows monthly spending for books and magazines. One plot shows monthly spending for tapes and CDs. One plot shows monthly spending for movie tickets.

Match the plots with the items. Which plot is for books and magazines? Which is for tapes and CDs? Which is for movie tickets?

Fill in the correct title for each number-line plot.

1. Spending for: _____ in 1 month

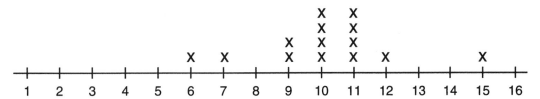

2. Spending for: _____ in 1 month

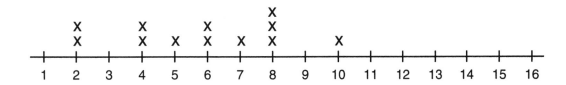

3. Spending for: _____ in 1 month

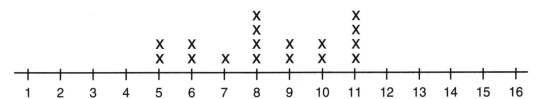

Constructing a Graph from Landmarks

1. Make up a list of data with the following landmarks:

Mode: 15   Minimum: 5   Median: 10   Maximum: 20

Use at least 10 numbers.

_____

2. Draw a bar graph to represent your data.

_____
(title)

3. Describe a situation in which these data might actually occur.

_____

_____

_____

_____

Data Analysis

1. Describe a situation in which the data in the line plot below might occur. Then give the plot a title and a unit.

_____

_____

_____(title)_____ |_____(unit)

```
                              X
                              X   X                       X
            X         X       X X X X         X           X
    X       X         X   X   X X X X         X       X   X       X   X
   -+---+---+---+---+---+---+---+---+---+---+---+---+---+---+---+---+---+-
   77  78  79  80  81  82  83  84  85  86  87  88  89  90  91  92  93  94
```

2. Find the following landmarks for the data in the line plot.

   a. Minimum: _____   b. Maximum: _____   c. Mode: _____   d. Median: _____

3. Describe a situation in which the data in the stem-and-leaf plot shown below might occur. Then give the plot a title and a unit.

_____

_____

_____(title)_____ |_____(unit)

Stems (10s)	Leaves (1s)
3	2
4	0
5	1 3 7
6	0 4 5 6 6 6 7 9
7	1 3 8 8 9
8	0 2 2 5 5 8 8 9
9	0 2 2 5 5 8 9 9

4. Find the following landmarks for the data in the stem-and-leaf plot.

   a. Minimum: _____   b. Maximum: _____

   c. Mode: _____   d. Median: _____

Contour Map

The contour map below shows the approximate percentage of sunny or partly sunny days for the months of December through February.

Percent of Sunny or Partly Sunny Days
December – February

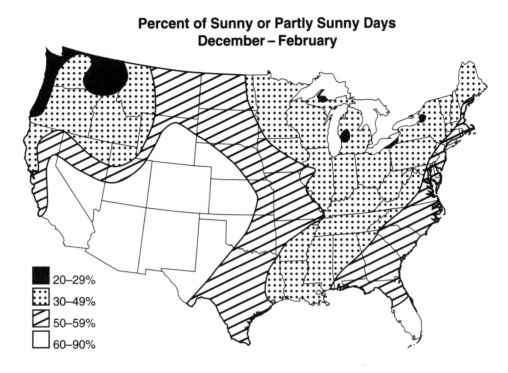

20–29%
30–49%
50–59%
60–90%

1. States where at least part of the state has sunny days more than 60% of the time between December and February.

   O Washington   O Florida   O Arizona   O New York

2. States that border the Pacific Ocean where, in some part of the state, more than 70% of the days are NOT sunny between December and February.

   O California   O Oregon   O Montana   O Washington

3. On the back of this page, make up your own question about the map. Answer your question.

Challenge

4. States with several regions where the amount of sunshine varies. Part of the state is sunny most of the time, but another part of the state is NOT sunny most of the time.

   O Utah   O Ohio   O Wyoming   O Wisconsin

Fraction Problems

1. To maintain their energy during the racing season, professional bicycle racers eat between 6,000 and 8,000 calories per day.

   About $\frac{3}{20}$ of these calories come from fat, and about $\frac{5}{20}$ come from protein. The remaining calories come from carbohydrates.

   What fraction of a bicycle racer's calories comes from carbohydrates? _____

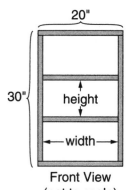

carbohydrates

$\frac{5}{20}$ protein

$\frac{3}{20}$ fat

2. Study the plan at the right for a small bookcase.

   All boards are $\frac{3}{4}$-inch thick.

   What is the width of each shelf? _____ inches

   If the shelves are evenly spaced, what is the height of the opening for each of the 3 spaces? _____ inches

   20"

   30" { height

   ← width →

   Front View
   (not to scale)

Each square in the grid at the right represents a city block. Each side of a block is $\frac{1}{8}$ mile long (that is, in this city, there are 8 blocks to each mile).

The distances below are measured along the sides of blocks.

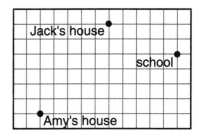

Jack's house

school

Amy's house

3. The distance from Amy's house to school is

   _____ blocks, or _____ mile(s).

4. The distance from Jack's house to school is

   _____ blocks, or _____ mile(s).

5. How much farther from school is Amy's house than Jack's house? _____ mile(s)

6. Amy walks from school to Jack's house and then home.

   How far is that? _____ mile(s).

Unit 7: Exponents and Negative Numbers

In this unit, your child will be introduced to exponential and scientific notation as a way of naming very large and very small numbers. These topics will become increasingly important later on, when your child begins work with algebra concepts. If you and your child have enjoyed playing math games in the past, you might want to play *Exponent Ball* during these lessons.

Your child will also review how parentheses are used to make expressions unambiguous and will be introduced to rules that determine in what order the operations in a mathematical expression must be performed.

Finally, your child will investigate why negative numbers were invented and learn to work with positive and negative numbers, using a variety of strategies. For example, your child will use number lines to compare, add, and subtract positive and negative numbers; use a slide rule to add and subtract positive and negative numbers; and use red and black counters to represent positive and negative numbers to model addition and subtraction problems.

The activities with counters are especially instructive. Counters are used to represent an account balance. The red counters (−$1) represent a debit, the black counters (+$1), a credit. If there are more red counters than black ones, the account is "in the red;" that is, the balance is negative. On the other hand, if there are more black counters than red ones, the account is "in the black;" that is, the balance is positive. By adding or subtracting red and black counters from an existing account balance, your child can model addition and subtraction of positive and negative numbers. To assist your child, you may want to explain how a checking or savings account works.

Please keep this Family Letter for reference as your child works through Unit 7.

Vocabulary

Important terms in Unit 7:

account balance An amount of money that you have or that you owe.

exponential notation A way to show repeated multiplication by the same factor. For example, 2^3 is exponential notation for $2 * 2 * 2$.

expression A group of mathematical symbols that represents a number—or can represent a number if values are assigned to any variables in the expression.

"in the black" Having a positive balance; having more money than is owed.

"in the red" Having a negative balance; owing more money than is available.

negative number A number that is less than zero.

nested parentheses Parentheses inside parentheses.

> *Example*
> $((6 * 4) - 2) / 2 = 11$

number-and-word notation A way of writing a large number using a combination of numbers and words. For example, *27 billion* is number-and-word notation for 27,000,000,000.

opposite of a number A number that is the same distance from 0 on the number line as a given number, but on the opposite side of 0. For example, the opposite of $+3$ is -3; the opposite of -5 is $+5$.

order of operations Rules that tell in what order to perform operations in arithmetic and algebra. The order of operations is:

1. Do the operations in parentheses first. (Use rules 2–4 inside the parentheses.)
2. Calculate all the expressions with exponents.
3. Multiply and divide in order from left to right.
4. Add and subtract in order from left to right.

parentheses Grouping symbols, ( ), used to tell which parts of an expression should be calculated first.

scientific notation A system for writing numbers in which a number is written as the product of a *power* of 10 and a number that is at least 1 and less than 10. Scientific notation allows you to write big and small numbers with only a few symbols. For example, $4 * 10^{12}$ is scientific notation for 4,000,000,000,000.

slide rule A tool used to perform calculations.

standard notation The most familiar way of representing whole numbers, integers, and decimals. In standard notation, the value of each digit depends on where the digit is in the number. For example, standard notation for three hundred fifty-six is 356.

Use with Lesson 6.11.

Do-Anytime Activities

To work with your child on the concepts taught in this unit and in previous units, try these interesting and rewarding activities:

1 Have your child pick out a stock from the stock-market pages of a newspaper. Encourage your child to watch the stock over a period of time and to report the change in stock prices daily, using positive and negative numbers.

2 Using the same stock in Activity 1, have your child write the high and low of that stock for each day. After your child has watched the stock over a period of time, have him or her find

- the *maximum* value observed.
- the *minimum* value observed.
- the *range* in values.
- the *mode,* if there is one.
- the *median* value observed.

3 Review tessellations with your child. Encourage your child to name the regular tessellations and to draw and name the 8 semiregular tessellations. Challenge your child to create Escher-type translation tessellations. You may want to go to the library first, and show your child examples of Escher's work.

4 Practice finding perimeters of objects and circumferences of circular objects around your home.

Building Skills through Games

In Unit 7, your child will practice operations and computation skills by playing the following games. For detailed instructions, see the *Student Reference Book.*

Name That Number See *Student Reference Book,* page 286
A game for two or three players using the Everything Math Deck or a complete deck of number cards. Playing *Name That Number* helps students review operations with whole numbers.

Scientific-Notation Toss See *Student Reference Book,* page 290
Two players will need 2 six-sided dice to play this game. This game develops skill in converting numbers from scientific notation to standard notation.

Top-It See *Student Reference Book,* page 296
The two versions of this game provide practice in adding and subtracting positive and negative numbers. Two to four players need a complete deck of number cards to play the game.

As You Help Your Child with Homework

As your child brings assignments home, you may want to go over the instructions together, clarifying them as necessary. The answers listed below will guide you through this unit's Study Links.

Study Link 7.1

1. Answers vary.
2. 1,838,265,625
3. **a.** yes
   b. Sample answer: There are more possible license plates (about 2 billion) than there are vehicles (about 200 million)
4. 1,728
5. 6,561
6. 537,824
7. 2,985,984

Study Link 7.2

1. billion
2. 10^3
3. trillion
4. 10^6
5. thousand; 10^3
6. million; 10^6
7. Sample answer: About 17 hours; About 2 years; About 2,000 years; About 2 million years

Study Link 7.3

1. 600; 3
2. 6
3. 500 million
4. 1 billion
5. 10 million

Study Link 7.4

1. $2 = (3 * 2) - (4 / 1)$
2. $3 = (4 + 3 - 1) / 2$
3. $4 = (3 - 1) + (4 / 2)$
4. $5 = (3 + 4 - 2) / 1$
5. $9 = (4 / 1) + 3 + 2$
6. $10 = 3 + (4 * 2) - 1$
8. $1 = ((4 + 1) - 3) / 2$
9. $6 = (1 + (4 * 2)) - 3$
10. $7 = ((4 * 3) / 2) + 1$
11. $8 = ((3 - 1) * 2) + 4$

Study Link 7.5

1. 34
2. 25
3. 28
4. 30
5. 21
6. 28
7. false
8. true
9. true
10. true
11. false
12. true
13. false
14. true
15. Story 1: $(2 * 8) + 4$; Story 2: $2 * (8 + 4)$

Study Link 7.6

For Problems 1–4, sample answers:

1. 2.6
2. 1.58
3. −5.5
4. −9.8
5. $-1.2, -1, 3.8, 5\frac{1}{4}, 5\frac{3}{8}$

6. $-7, -6, -4\frac{1}{2}, -0.5, 0$
7. F
8. F
9. T
10. T
11. T

For Problems 12–15, sample answers:

12. $-1 < 1$; T
13. $-5 = -\frac{500}{100}$; T
14. $-\frac{1}{2} = 2^2 - 1\frac{1}{2}$; F
15. $-3 > -1$; F

Study Link 7.7

1. $<$
2. $>$
3. $>$
4. $>$
5. $2 debt
6. $5 cash
7. -9
8. 22
9. -88
10. 70
11. 3
12. $-9,000$

Study Link 7.8

1. -41
2. 43
3. 0
4. -8
5. 40
6. 20
7. -85
8. -0.5
9. 3.0
10. 2
11. (-15)
12. (-10)

Study Link 7.9

1. $<$
2. $>$
3. $>$
4. $>$
5. $>$
6. $>$
7. -5
8. -21
9. 4
10. -6
11. -11
12. -26
13. 16
14. -4
15. T
16. T
17. $(-2 + 3) * 4 = 4$
18. T
19. $-3 + 5 * (2 - (-6)) = 37$
20. $4^2 + ((-3) - (5)) * 2 = 20$
21. 10:04 A.M.

Study Link 7.10

1. $-5 - (-58) = 53$
2. 10^6
3. 10^4
4. 10^5
5. 10^9
6. 3,000,000
7. 20,000
8. 640,000
9. 2,600,000
10. $8 * 10^6$
11. $7 * 10^9$
12. $3 * 10^3$
13. $17 * 10^{10}$
14. Number model: $3 * 6 - 5 = 13$;
    Answer: 13 containers
15. above; Number model: $-\frac{5}{8} + \frac{6}{8} = \frac{1}{8}$
    Answer: $\frac{1}{8}$ inch above

Use with Lesson 6.11.

Counting License Plates

Automobile license plates can include letters, numbers, or a combination of letters and numbers. The letter O is usually not used because it might be confused with the number zero. This leaves 35 different characters.

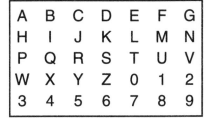

In many states, license plates consist of 6 characters. There are 35 choices for each character.

A	B	C	D	E	F	G
H	I	J	K	L	M	N
P	Q	R	S	T	U	V
W	X	Y	Z	0	1	2
3	4	5	6	7	8	9

35 choices for each character

1. List three possible 6-character license plates.

   a. _____ _____ _____ _____ _____ _____

   b. _____ _____ _____ _____ _____ _____

   c. _____ _____ _____ _____ _____ _____

2. The total number of possible license plates can be found by using 35 as a factor 6 times.

   $$35 * 35 * 35 * 35 * 35 * 35, \text{ or } 35^6$$

   If your calculator can display up to 10 digits, find 35^6, the number of possible different six-character license plates. _____

Challenge

In 1997, there were 207,754,000 registered motor vehicles in the United States.

3. a. Could every registered motor vehicle in the United States have a different six-character license plate? _____

   b. Explain how you found the answer.

   _____

   _____

Practice

Use your calculator to write the following numbers in standard notation.

4. $12 * 12 * 12 =$ _____

5. $9 * 9 * 9 * 9 =$ _____

6. $14^5 =$ _____

7. 12 to the sixth power $=$ _____

Guides for Powers of 10

There are prefixes that name powers of 10. You know some of them from the metric system; for example, *kilo-* in "kilometer" (1,000 meters). It's helpful to memorize the prefixes for every third power of 10 through one trillion.

Memorize the table below. Have a friend quiz you. Then cover the table and try to complete the statements below.

Standard Notation	Number-and-Word Notation	Exponential Notation	Prefix
1,000	1 thousand	10^3	kilo-
1,000,000	1 million	10^6	mega-
1,000,000,000	1 billion	10^9	giga-
1,000,000,000,000	1 trillion	10^{12}	tera-

1. More than 10^9 or one _____ people live in China.

2. One thousand or $10^{\boxed{}}$ feet is a little less than $\frac{1}{5}$ of a mile.

3. Astronomers estimate that there are more than 10^{12} or one

_____ stars in the universe.

4. More than one million or $10^{\boxed{}}$ copies of *The New York Times* are sold every day.

5. A kiloton equals one _____ or $10^{\boxed{}}$ metric tons.

6. A megaton equals one _____ or $10^{\boxed{}}$ metric tons.

Challenge

7. How far back in time would you travel if you went back

    a. 10^3 minutes? _____

    b. 10^6 minutes? _____

    c. 10^9 minutes? _____

    d. 10^{12} minutes? _____

(Remember that a million is 1,000 thousands; a billion is 1,000 millions; and a trillion is 1,000 billions.)

Interpreting Scientific Notation

Scientific notation is a short way to represent large and small numbers. In scientific notation, a number is written as the product of two factors. One factor is a whole number or decimal. The other factor is a power of 10.

Scientific notation: $4 * 10^4$

         Meaning: Multiply 10^4 (10,000) by 4.

                 $4 * 10^4 = 4 * 10,000 = 40,000$

Scientific notation: $6 * 10^6$

         Meaning: Multiply 10^6 (1,000,000) by 6.

                 $6 * 10^6 = 6 * 1,000,000 = 6,000,000$

Guides for Powers of 10	
10^3	one thousand
10^6	one million
10^9	one billion
10^{12}	one trillion

Complete the following statements.

1. The area of Alaska is about $6 * 10^5$ or _____ thousand square miles.

The area of the "lower 48" states is about $3 * 10^6$ or _____ million square miles.

2. There are about $6 * 10^9$ or _____ billion people in the world.

3. It is estimated that about $5 * 10^8$ or _____ people speak English as their first or second language.

4. The language spoken by the greatest number of people is Chinese.

More than $1 * 10^9$ or _____ people speak Chinese.

5. It is estimated that the most popular television shows in the United States are watched by at least one person in

each of $1 * 10^7$ or _____ households.

Source: The World Almanac and Book of Facts, 2000

Different Ways to Write 1 through 10

Make each sentence true by inserting parentheses.

SRB
203–204

1. $2 = 3 * 2 - 4 / 1$ **2.** $3 = 4 + 3 - 1 / 2$ **3.** $4 = 3 - 1 + 4 / 2$

4. $5 = 3 + 4 - 2 / 1$ **5.** $9 = 4 / 1 + 3 + 2$ **6.** $10 = 3 + 4 * 2 - 1$

7. Write seven different names for the number 8. Use only numbers less than 10, and use at least three different operations in each name. Use parentheses.

8

Problem 12 tells how to
fill in the last 2 names. ⎫

Challenge

Make each sentence true by inserting parentheses. You will need at least two pairs of parentheses for each sentence. (*Reminder:* When you have a pair of parentheses inside another pair, the parentheses are called **nested parentheses.**)

Example $8 = 5 * 6 + 2 / 4$

Answer $8 = ((5 * 6) + 2) / 4$

8. $1 = 4 + 1 - 3 / 2$ **9.** $6 = 1 + 4 * 2 - 3$

10. $7 = 4 * 3 / 2 + 1$ **11.** $8 = 3 - 1 * 2 + 4$

12. Add two names to your name-collection box in Problem 7.
Use nested parentheses in your expressions.

Order of Operations

Rules for Order of Operations

(1) Do operations in parentheses.

(2) Calculate all exponential expressions.

(3) Do multiplications and divisions in order, from left to right.

(4) Do additions and subtractions in order, from left to right.

Solve.

1. $4 + 5 * 6 =$ _____

2. $(2 + 3)^2 =$ _____

3. $12 * 2 + 8 \div 2 =$ _____

4. $115 - 10^2 + 3 * 5 =$ _____

5. $6 * (3 + 2^2) \div 2 =$ _____

6. $7 + 9 * 7 \div 3 =$ _____

Write true or false for each number sentence. Follow the rules of order of operations.

7. $3 + 4 * 5 = 35$ _____

8. $(3 + 4) * 5 = 35$ _____

9. $0 = 3 * 4 - 12$ _____

10. $0 = (3 * 4) - 12$ _____

11. $36 = 12 - 3 * 4$ _____

12. $36 = (12 - 3) * 4$ _____

13. $8 \div 2 + 6 = 1$ _____

14. $8 \div (2 + 6) = 1$ _____

15. Match each story with the expression that fits it.

Story 1

Marlene and her friend Mandy each had eight pencils. They bought four more pencils.

Number of pencils in all:

$(2 * 8) + 4$

Story 2

Marlene bought 2 eight-packs of pencils. Four free pencils came with each pack.

$2 * (8 + 4)$

Greater Than or Less Than?

Name a number between each pair of numbers.

1. 2 and 3 _____

2. 1.5 and 2 _____

3. -5 and -6 _____

4. -9.5 and -10 _____

Order each set of numbers from *least* to *greatest*.

5. $5\frac{1}{4}$, 3.8, -1.2, -1, $5\frac{3}{8}$ _____

6. -6, $-4\frac{1}{2}$, -0.5, -7, 0 _____

True or false? Write T for true and F for false.

7. $-6 > 5$ _____

8. $5\frac{1}{2} < 5\frac{3}{6}$ _____

9. $-2.5 > -3.5$ _____

10. $-4 < 0$ _____

11. 7 is greater than -7 _____

Write two true number sentences and two false number sentences. In each sentence, use at least one negative number and one of the symbols $>$, $<$, or $=$. Label each sentence T or F.

12. _____ _____

13. _____ _____

14. _____ _____

15. _____ _____

Use with Lesson 7.6.

151

Positive and Negative Numbers

Write < or >.

1. −7 _____ 6

2. 0.01 _____ −32

3. 8.5 _____ −10³

4. −$\frac{3}{4}$ _____ −1.6

Find the account balance. ⊞ = $1 cash. ⊟ = $1 debt.

5. Balance = $ _____

6. Balance = $ _____

Solve these addition problems.

7. −15 + 6 = _____

8. 17 + (−5) = _____

9. −56 + (−32) = _____

10. 90 + (−20) = _____

11. 18 + (−15) = _____

12. −987 + 987 = _____

13. Use the rule to complete the table.

| −200 |
| in ↓ |
| **Rule** |
| out = −25 + in |
| out ↓ |
| −225 |

in	out
25	
50	
−25	
−100	
100	
0	

Addition and Subtraction Problems

Reminder:
To subtract a number, you can add the opposite of that number.

Solve each problem. Be careful. Some problems are additions and some are subtractions.

1. $-25 + (-16) =$ _____

2. $0 - (-43) =$ _____

3. $-4 - (-4) =$ _____

4. $-4 - 4 =$ _____

5. $29 - (-11) =$ _____

6. $9 - (-11) =$ _____

7. $-100 + 15 =$ _____

8. $10 - 10.5 =$ _____

9. $9.7 + (-6.7) =$ _____

10. $4\frac{1}{2} + (-2\frac{1}{2}) =$ _____

11. $10 +$ _____ $= -5$

12. $10 -$ _____ $= 20$

13. For each temperature change in the table, two number models are shown in the "Temperature after Change" column. Only one of the number models is correct. Cross out the incorrect number model. Then complete the correct number model.

Temperature before Change	Temperature Change	Temperature after Change	
40°	up 7°	$40 + 7 =$ _____	$40 + (-7) =$ _____
10°	down 8°	$10 - (-8) =$ _____	$10 - 8 =$ _____
−15° (15° below zero)	up 10°	$-15 + 10 =$ _____	$15 + 10 =$ _____
−20° (20° below zero)	down 10°	$-20 - 10 =$ _____	$20 - (-10) =$ _____

Positive and Negative Number Review Study Link 7.9

Write >, < or =.

1. -8 _____ 5

2. -3 _____ -10

3. 10 _____ -20

4. 12 _____ -15

5. $-\frac{3}{4}$ _____ -1

6. 3^2 _____ 6

Add or subtract.

7. $-20 + 15 =$ _____

8. $-14 + (-7) =$ _____

9. $-8 + 12 =$ _____

10. $3 + (-9) =$ _____

11. $-4 - 7 =$ _____

12. $-10 - 16 =$ _____

13. $5 - (-11) =$ _____

14. $8 - 12 =$ _____

Some of the following number sentences are true because they follow the rules for the order of operations. Some of the sentences are false. Make a check mark next to the true number sentences. Insert parentheses in the false number sentences to make them true.

15. $3 + 7 * 5 = 38$

16. $-5 + 20 \div 5 = -1$

17. $-2 + 3 * 4 = 4$

18. $-2 + 3 * 4 = 10$

19. $-3 + 5 * 2 - (-6) = 37$

20. $4^2 + (-3) - (-5) * 2 = 20$

21. a. Julie arrived 20 minutes before the race began. She started right on time. It took her 24 minutes to finish the 6-kilometer race. She stayed 10 minutes after the race to cool off; then she left. If she arrived at the race at 9:10 A.M., what time was it when she left?

_____

b. Explain how you found your answer.

_____

_____

_____

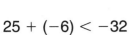

Unit 7 Review

1. Circle the number sentences that are true.

$25 + (-6) < -32$ $4^2 < 2^4$ $15 * 15 * 15 < 15^3$

$21 * 21 = 21^3$ $-5 - (-58) = 53$ $25 > 5^2 - (-2)$

Write each number as a power of 10.

2. 1,000,000 _____   **3.** 10,000 _____

4. 1 hundred-thousand _____   **5.** 1 billion _____

Match the number written in number-and-word notation with its standard notation. Fill in the oval next to the correct answer.

6. 3 million

   ○ 300,000

   ○ 30,000,000

   ○ 3,000,000

   ○ 30,000

7. 20 thousand

   ○ 200,000

   ○ 20,000

   ○ 2,000,000

   ○ 20,000,000

8. 640 thousand

   ○ 6,400,000

   ○ 64,000,000

   ○ 640,000,000

   ○ 640,000

9. 2.6 million

   ○ 26,000,000

   ○ 2,060,000

   ○ 20,600,000

   ○ 2,600,000

Unit 7 Review (cont.)

Write each number in scientific notation.

10. 8 million _____

11. 7 billion _____

12. 3 thousand _____

13. 17 billion _____

14. Louise bought three 6-pack containers of yogurt. She ate 5 individual containers of yogurt in one week. How many containers did she have left?

Number model: _____   Answer: _____

15. The water in Leroy's and Jerod's fish tank had evaporated so that it was about $\frac{5}{8}$ inch below the level it should be. They added water and the water level went up about $\frac{3}{4}$ inch. Did the water level end up above or below where it should be? _____

How much above or below?

Number model: _____   Answer: _____

Use with Lesson 7.10.

Family Letter

Unit 8: Fractions and Ratios

In Unit 4, your child reviewed equivalent fractions and developed multiplication and division rules for finding equivalent fractions.

In this unit, your child will apply this knowledge to operations with fractions and mixed numbers. Students will learn that the key to adding, subtracting, and dividing fractions with unlike denominators is to convert them into fractions with the same denominator.

Students will be introduced to fraction multiplication, using folded paper to represent fractions of a whole. Then the class will study fraction multiplication using "area models," which are diagrams that help students visualize dividing a "whole" into parts. This concept building will lead to an algorithm for multiplying fractions:

$$\frac{a}{b} * \frac{c}{d} = \frac{a * c}{b * d}$$

Example: $\frac{2}{5} * \frac{3}{4} = \frac{2 * 3}{5 * 4} = \frac{6}{20}$, or $\frac{3}{10}$

For mixed-number multiplication, students will first rename the mixed numbers as fractions, then use the multiplication of fractions algorithm to find their product, and finally rename the product as a mixed number.

Example: $2\frac{1}{2} * 1\frac{2}{3} = \frac{5}{2} * \frac{5}{3}$

$$= \frac{5 * 5}{2 * 3} = \frac{25}{6} = 4\frac{1}{6}$$

You might want to show your child another way to solve this problem, using partial products:

$2\frac{1}{2} * 1\frac{2}{3}$ can be thought of as $(2 + \frac{1}{2}) * (1 + \frac{2}{3})$. There are 4 partial products, indicated by arrows:

$$2 * 1 = 2$$

$(2 + \frac{1}{2}) * (1 + \frac{2}{3})$
$$2 * \frac{2}{3} = \frac{4}{3}$$
$$\frac{1}{2} * 1 = \frac{1}{2}$$
$$\frac{1}{2} * \frac{2}{3} = \frac{2}{6}$$

Add the partial products: $2 + \frac{4}{3} + \frac{1}{2} + \frac{2}{6} = 2 + \frac{8}{6} + \frac{3}{6} + \frac{2}{6} = 2 + \frac{13}{6} = 4\frac{1}{6}$

Your child will play several games, such as *Build-It* and *Fraction Action, Fraction Friction,* to practice sorting fractions and adding fractions with unlike denominators.

Finally, as part of the American Tour, students will participate in data explorations involving population distributions and household sizes.

Please keep this Family Letter for reference as your child works through Unit 8.

Vocabulary

Important terms in Unit 8:

area model A model for multiplication problems, in which the length and width of a rectangle represent the factors and the area represents the product.

discount The amount by which the regular price of an item is reduced. For example, if a $10 item is on sale for $7, the discount is $3. The discount accounts for 3\10, or 30% of the full price. We say that the percent of discount is 30%.

horizontal Positioned in a left-to-right orientation; parallel to the horizon.

majority A number or amount that is more than half of a total number or amount.

unit fraction A fraction whose numerator is 1. For example, $\frac{1}{2}$, $\frac{1}{3}$, $\frac{1}{8}$, and $\frac{1}{20}$ are all unit fractions.

unit percent One percent (1%).

vertical Positioned in an up-down orientation; perpendicular to the horizon.

Building Skills through Games

In Unit 8, your child will practice skills with fractions and other numbers by playing the following games. For detailed instructions for many games, see the *Student Reference Book*.

Build-It See *Student Reference Book*, p. 263
This game for partners requires a deck of 16 Build–It fraction cards. This game provides practice in comparing and ordering fractions.

Fraction Capture See *Math Masters*, p. 87
Partners roll dice to form fractions and then attempt to capture squares on a Fraction Capture Game Board. This game provides practice in finding equivalent fractions and in adding fractions.

Mixed Number Spin (*Math Masters*, p. 105) **and *Fraction Spin*** (*Math Masters*, p. 110)
Partners use a spinner to randomly select fractions and mixed numbers that are used to complete number sentences. This game provides practice in adding and subtracting fractions and mixed numbers.

Fraction Action/Fraction Friction See *Student Reference Book*, p. 277
This game for partners requires a set of 16 Fraction Action, Fraction Friction cards. The game is similar to blackjack, and provides practice in adding fractions with unlike denominators.

Fraction Multiplication Top-It and ***Fraction/Whole-Number Multiplication Top-It***
Partners play a card game using fraction cards. This game provides practice in multiplying fractions and multiplying whole numbers and fractions.

Name That Number See *Student Reference Book*, p. 286
Partners play a card game using a deck of number cards. These games provide practice in using order of operations to write number sentences.

Frac-Tac-Toe See *Student Reference Book*, p. 274–276
This game for partners requires a deck of number cards 0–10 and a Game Board that is similar to a bingo card. The game provides practice in converting among fractions, decimals, and percents.

Use with Lesson 7.11.

Do-Anytime Activities

To work with your child on the concepts taught in this unit and in previous units, try these interesting and rewarding activities:

1 Ask your child to measure the lengths of two objects using a ruler. Then ask him or her to calculate the sum and difference of their lengths.

2 Ask your child to explain how to use the fraction operation keys on his or her calculator. For example, ask your child to show you how to enter fractions and mixed numbers, simplify fractions, and convert between fractions and decimals.

3 Help your child identify advertisements in signs, newspapers, and magazines that use percents. Help your child find the sale price of an item that is discounted by a certain percent; for example, a $40 shirt reduced by 25% costs $30.

As You Help Your Child with Homework

As your child brings assignments home, you may want to go over the instructions together, clarifying them as necessary. The answers listed below will guide you through this unit's Study Links.

Study Link 8.1

1. $\frac{3}{6}$ **2.** $\frac{2}{3}$ **3.** $\frac{5}{6}$

4. $\frac{19}{20}$ **5.** $\frac{9}{17}$ **6.** $\frac{4}{7}$

7. Sample answer: A common denominator is 21 * 17, or 357. $\frac{11}{21} = \frac{11 * 17}{21 * 17} = \frac{187}{357}$, and $\frac{9}{17} = \frac{9 * 21}{17 * 21} = \frac{189}{357}$. So $\frac{9}{17}$ is greater.

8. 0.75   **9.** $0.\overline{6}$ **10.** 0.625

11. 0.7   **12.** 0.55   **13.** 0.84

14. Sample answer: $\frac{1}{8}$ is half of $\frac{1}{4}$ $\left(\frac{0.25}{2} = 0.125\right)$. $\frac{5}{8} = \frac{4}{8} + \frac{1}{8} = 0.5 + 0.125$, or 0.625.

15. >   **16.** =   **17.** >

18. >   **19.** >   **20.** >

21. Sample answer: $\frac{6}{7} + \frac{1}{7} = 1$. $\frac{1}{8}$ is less than $\frac{1}{7}$, so $\frac{6}{7} + \frac{1}{8}$ is less than 1.

Study Link 8.2

2. 2   **3.** $10\frac{2}{3}$ **5.** $5\frac{1}{2}$

7. 6   **9.** 14   **11.** $5\frac{1}{4}$

13. $9\frac{3}{8}$ **15.** $8\frac{1}{4}$

Study Link 8.3

1. 11   **3.** 10   **6.** $6\frac{5}{3}$

7. $2\frac{1}{2}$ **9.** $2\frac{1}{5}$ **11.** $5\frac{4}{9}$

13. $2\frac{1}{4}$ **15.** $\frac{1}{2}$

Study Link 8.4

1. $\frac{4}{5}$; $\frac{155}{200}$ **2.** $< \frac{1}{2}$ **3.** $> \frac{1}{2}$

4. $= \frac{1}{2}$ **5.** $< \frac{1}{2}$

6. $\dfrac{\boxed{6}}{\boxed{1}} + \dfrac{\langle 5 \rangle}{\boxed{6}} = \frac{41}{6} = 6\frac{5}{6}$

Study Link 8.5

1. $\frac{6}{15}$, or $\frac{2}{5}$ **3.** $\frac{12}{20}$, or $\frac{3}{5}$

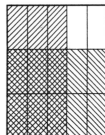   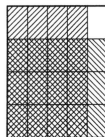

5. Nina: $\frac{1}{2}$; Phillip: $\frac{1}{6}$; Ezra: $\frac{1}{6}$; Benjamin: $\frac{1}{6}$

Study Link 8.6

1. $\frac{1}{3} * \frac{2}{5} = \frac{2}{15}$

3. $\frac{7}{8} * \frac{1}{3} = \frac{7}{24}$

5. $\frac{10}{18}$, or $\frac{5}{9}$

7. $\frac{12}{25}$

9. $\frac{5}{63}$

11. 9; 3

Study Link 8.7

1.

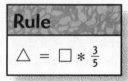

in □	out △
$\frac{1}{2}$	$\frac{3}{10}$
2	$\frac{6}{5}$, or $1\frac{1}{5}$
$\frac{4}{5}$	$\frac{12}{25}$
$\frac{3}{4}$	$\frac{9}{20}$
3	$\frac{9}{5}$, or $1\frac{4}{5}$

3.

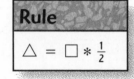

in □	out △
$\frac{2}{3}$	$\frac{2}{6}$
$\frac{3}{4}$	$\frac{3}{8}$
$\frac{7}{8}$	$\frac{7}{16}$
3	$1\frac{1}{2}$

5. Rules and tables vary.

Study Link 8.8

1. a. $\frac{46}{24}$, or $1\frac{11}{12}$ b. $\frac{10}{40}$, or $\frac{1}{4}$

   c. $\frac{85}{24}$, or $3\frac{13}{24}$ d. $\frac{175}{24}$, or $7\frac{7}{24}$

   e. $\frac{296}{60}$, or $4\frac{14}{15}$ f. $\frac{364}{40}$, or $9\frac{1}{10}$

2. a. $8\frac{5}{9}$ b. $5\frac{1}{2}$ c. $2\frac{1}{12}$

3. a. 5   b. $5\frac{5}{8}$

Study Link 8.9

1. $\frac{45}{100}$; 0.45; 45%

   $\frac{3}{10}$; 0.3; 30%

   $\frac{2}{10}$; 0.2; 20%

   $\frac{15}{100}$; 0.15; 15%

2. Calculated discounts: $100.00; $1,600.00; $7.84; $0.75; $8.70; $5.28; $810.00; $385.00

Study Link 8.10

1. 4; 20   3. 1,200 miles

5. 32 cookies   7. yes

9. $350; $70

Study Link 8.11

Sample answers for Problems 1–4:

1. $\frac{14}{16}$, $\frac{28}{32}$, $\frac{35}{40}$ 2. $\frac{6}{8}$, $\frac{9}{12}$, $\frac{12}{16}$

3. $\frac{1}{2}$, $\frac{2}{4}$, $\frac{3}{6}$ 4. $\frac{4}{6}$, $\frac{6}{9}$, $\frac{8}{12}$

5. $\frac{3}{8}$ 6. $\frac{5}{9}$

7. $\frac{7}{9}$ 8. $\frac{7}{12}$

9. Sample answer: I changed $\frac{4}{10}$ and $\frac{7}{12}$ to fractions with a common denominator. $\frac{4}{10} = \frac{24}{60}$ and $\frac{7}{12} = \frac{35}{60}$. Since $\frac{1}{2} = \frac{30}{60}$, $\frac{7}{12}$ is $\frac{5}{60}$ away from $\frac{1}{2}$ and $\frac{4}{10}$ is $\frac{6}{60}$ away from $\frac{1}{2}$. So, $\frac{7}{12}$ is closer to $\frac{1}{2}$.

11. $\frac{13}{20}$ 13. $\frac{11}{18}$

15. $\frac{17}{24}$ 17. $\frac{3}{10}$

19. $3\frac{1}{3}$

Study Link 8.12

1. 27   3. 5

5. $3\frac{4}{5}$ 7. $1\frac{5}{9}$

9. $8\frac{5}{12}$ 11. 6

13. $11\frac{1}{4}$ 15. $4\frac{1}{2}$

Comparing Fractions

SRB
66–68
83–88

Circle the greater fraction for each pair.

1. $\frac{3}{8}$ or $\frac{3}{6}$

2. $\frac{2}{3}$ or $\frac{2}{9}$

3. $\frac{4}{7}$ or $\frac{5}{6}$

4. $\frac{19}{20}$ or $\frac{4}{8}$

5. $\frac{11}{21}$ or $\frac{9}{17}$

6. $\frac{4}{7}$ or $\frac{6}{11}$

7. Explain how you got your answer for Problem 5.

_____

_____

_____

Write the decimal equivalent for each fraction.

8. $\frac{3}{4} = $ _____

9. $\frac{2}{3} = $ _____

10. $\frac{5}{8} = $ _____

11. $\frac{7}{10} = $ _____

12. $\frac{11}{20} = $ _____

13. $\frac{21}{25} = $ _____

14. Explain how you can do Problem 10 without using a calculator.

_____

_____

Use >, <, or = to make each number sentence true.

15. $\frac{1}{2} + \frac{5}{8}$ _____ 1

16. $\frac{2}{3} + \frac{2}{6}$ _____ 1

17. $\frac{7}{9} + \frac{3}{5}$ _____ 1

18. 1 _____ $\frac{6}{10} + \frac{5}{20}$

19. 1 _____ $\frac{3}{8} + \frac{4}{9}$

20. 1 _____ $\frac{6}{7} + \frac{1}{8}$

21. Explain how you found the answer to Problem 20.

_____

_____

_____

Subtraction of Mixed Numbers

Fill in the missing numbers.

1. $3\frac{3}{8} = 2\frac{\square}{8}$

2. $4\frac{5}{6} = \square\frac{11}{6}$

3. $2\frac{1}{9} = 1\frac{\square}{9}$

4. $6\frac{3}{7} = \square\frac{10}{7}$

5. $4\frac{3}{5} = 3\frac{\square}{5}$

6. $7\frac{2}{3} = \square\frac{\square}{3}$

Subtract. Write your answers in simplest form.

7. $\begin{array}{r} 5\frac{3}{4} \\ -\ 3\frac{1}{4} \\ \hline \end{array}$

8. $\begin{array}{r} 6\frac{2}{3} \\ -\ 4\frac{1}{3} \\ \hline \end{array}$

9. $\begin{array}{r} 5\frac{4}{5} \\ -\ 3\frac{3}{5} \\ \hline \end{array}$

10. $4 - \frac{3}{8} =$ _____

11. $6 - \frac{5}{9} =$ _____

12. $5 - 2\frac{3}{10} =$ _____

13. $7 - 4\frac{3}{4} =$ _____

14. $3\frac{2}{5} - 1\frac{3}{5} =$ _____

15. $4\frac{3}{8} - 3\frac{7}{8} =$ _____

More Fraction Problems

1. Circle all the fractions below that are greater than $\frac{3}{4}$.

$\frac{4}{5}$ $\frac{13}{20}$ $\frac{1}{2}$ $\frac{18}{25}$ $\frac{9}{12}$ $\frac{155}{200}$ $\frac{7}{11}$

Decide whether the sum or difference is greater than $\frac{1}{2}$, less than $\frac{1}{2}$, or equal to $\frac{1}{2}$. Circle your answer. (*Hint:* Find a common denominator for each problem.)

2. $\frac{1}{10} + \frac{2}{7}$ $> \frac{1}{2}$ $< \frac{1}{2}$ $= \frac{1}{2}$

3. $\frac{5}{6} - \frac{1}{4}$ $> \frac{1}{2}$ $< \frac{1}{2}$ $= \frac{1}{2}$

4. $\frac{18}{20} - \frac{2}{5}$ $> \frac{1}{2}$ $< \frac{1}{2}$ $= \frac{1}{2}$

5. $\frac{3}{4} - \frac{1}{3}$ $> \frac{1}{2}$ $< \frac{1}{2}$ $= \frac{1}{2}$

Fraction Puzzle

Goal To select and place three different numbers so that the sum is as large as possible.

Procedure Select three different numbers from this list: 1, 2, 3, 4, 5, 6.

- Write the same number in each square.

- Write a different number in the circle.

- Write a third number in the hexagon.

- Add the two fractions.

Example If ☐ = 2, ⬡ = 3, and ◯ = 4, then the sum is 2.

$$\frac{2}{4} + \frac{3}{2} = \frac{8}{4} = 2$$

Fractions of Fractions

Example

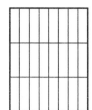   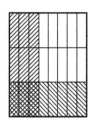

The whole rectangle represents ONE.

Shade $\frac{3}{8}$ of the interior.

Shade $\frac{1}{3}$ of the interior in a different way.

The double shading shows that $\frac{1}{3}$ of $\frac{3}{8}$ is $\frac{3}{24}$, or $\frac{1}{8}$.

In each of the following problems, the whole rectangle represents ONE.

1. Shade $\frac{3}{5}$ of the interior.

Shade $\frac{2}{3}$ of the interior in a different way.

The double shading shows that

$\frac{2}{3}$ of $\frac{3}{5}$ is _____.

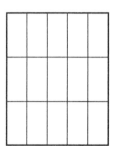

2. Shade $\frac{3}{4}$ of the interior.

Shade $\frac{1}{3}$ of the interior in a different way.

The double shading shows that

$\frac{1}{3}$ of $\frac{3}{4}$ is _____.

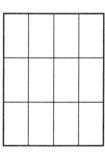

3. Shade $\frac{4}{5}$.

Shade $\frac{3}{4}$ of the interior in a different way.

The double shading shows that

$\frac{3}{4}$ of $\frac{4}{5}$ is _____.

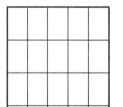

4. Shade $\frac{5}{8}$.

Shade $\frac{3}{5}$ of the interior in a different way.

The double shading shows that

$\frac{3}{5}$ of $\frac{5}{8}$ is _____.

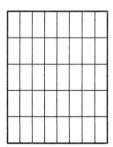

5. Nina and Phillip cut Mr. Ferguson's lawn. Nina worked alone on her half, but Phillip shared his half equally with his friends, Ezra and Benjamin. What fraction of the earnings should each person get?

Multiplying Fractions

Write a number model for each area model.

Example

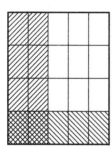

$\frac{1}{4} * \frac{2}{5} = \frac{2}{20}$, or $\frac{1}{10}$

1.

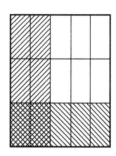

_____

2.

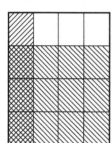

_____

3.

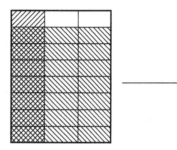

_____

Multiply.

4. $\frac{3}{7} * \frac{2}{10} =$ _____

5. $\frac{5}{6} * \frac{2}{3} =$ _____

6. $\frac{1}{2} * \frac{1}{4} =$ _____

7. $\frac{4}{5} * \frac{3}{5} =$ _____

8. $\frac{2}{3} * \frac{3}{8} =$ _____

9. $\frac{1}{7} * \frac{5}{9} =$ _____

10. Matt is making cookies for the school fund-raiser. The recipe calls for $\frac{2}{3}$ cup of chocolate chips. He decides to triple the recipe. How many cups of chocolate chips does he need?   _____ cups

11. The total number of goals scored by both teams in the field-hockey game was 15. Julie's team scored $\frac{3}{5}$ of the goals. Julie scored $\frac{1}{3}$ of her team's goals. How many goals did Julie's team score?   _____ goals

How many goals did Julie score?   _____ goals

12. Girls are one-half of the fifth grade class. Two-tenths of these girls have red hair. Red-haired girls are what fraction of the fifth grade class?

_____

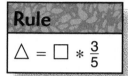 **"What's My Rule?"**

Use the given rule to complete each table.

1. | Rule |
| --- |
| $\triangle = \square * \frac{3}{5}$ |

in ($\square$)	out ($\triangle$)
$\frac{1}{2}$	
2	
$\frac{4}{5}$	
$\frac{3}{4}$	
3	

2. | Rule |
| --- |
| $\triangle = \square * 4$ |

in ($\square$)	out ($\triangle$)
$\frac{2}{3}$	
$\frac{4}{5}$	
$\frac{8}{9}$	
$\frac{5}{4}$	
$\frac{7}{3}$	

What is the rule for each table?

3. | Rule |
| --- |
| |

in ($\square$)	out ($\triangle$)
$\frac{2}{3}$	$\frac{2}{6}$
$\frac{3}{4}$	$\frac{3}{8}$
$\frac{7}{8}$	$\frac{7}{16}$
3	$1\frac{1}{2}$

4. | Rule |
| --- |
| |

in ($\square$)	out ($\triangle$)
2	$\frac{1}{2}$
3	$\frac{3}{4}$
$\frac{5}{6}$	$\frac{5}{24}$
$\frac{2}{3}$	$\frac{1}{6}$

5. Make and complete your own "What's My Rule?" table on the back of this page.

Multiplying Fractions and Mixed Numbers Study Link 8.8

1. Multiply.

a. $5\frac{3}{4} * \frac{2}{6} =$ _____

b. $\frac{5}{8} * \frac{2}{5} =$ _____

c. $4\frac{1}{4} * \frac{5}{6} =$ _____

d. $2\frac{1}{3} * 3\frac{1}{8} =$ _____

e. $3\frac{1}{12} * 1\frac{3}{5} =$ _____

f. $2\frac{4}{5} * 3\frac{2}{8} =$ _____

2. Find the area of each figure below.

Area of a Rectangle	Area of a Triangle	Area of a Parallelogram
$A = b * h$	$A = \frac{1}{2} * b * h$	$A = b * h$

a.

$2\frac{1}{3}$ yd
$3\frac{2}{3}$ yd

b.
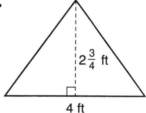
$2\frac{3}{4}$ ft
4 ft

c.
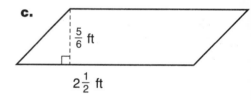
$\frac{5}{6}$ ft
$2\frac{1}{2}$ ft

Area = _____ yd²

Area = _____ ft²

Area = _____ ft²

3. The dimensions of a large doghouse are $2\frac{1}{2}$ times the dimensions of a small doghouse.

a. If the width of the small doghouse is 2 feet, what is the width of the large doghouse?

_____ feet

b. If the length of the small doghouse is $2\frac{1}{4}$ feet, what is the length of the large doghouse?

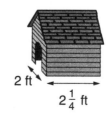

2 ft

$2\frac{1}{4}$ ft

_____ feet

Fractions, Decimals, and Percents

1. Complete the table so that each number is shown as a fraction, decimal, and percent.

Fraction	Decimal	Percent
		45%
	0.3	
$\frac{2}{10}$		
	0.15	

2. Use your percent sense to estimate the discount for each item. Then calculate the discount for each item. (If necessary, round to the nearest cent.)

Item	List Price	Percent of Discount	Estimated Discount	Calculated Discount
Saguaro cactus with arms	$400.00	25%		
Life-sized wax figure of yourself	$10,000.00	16%		
Manhole cover	$78.35	10%		
Live scorpion	$14.98	5%		
10,000 honeybees	$29.00	30%		
Dinner for one on the Eiffel Tower	$88.00	6%		
Magician's box for sawing a person in half	$4,500.00	18%		
Fire hydrant	$1,100.00	35%		

Source: Everything Has Its Price

Unit Fractions

Finding the worth of the unit fraction will help you to solve each problem below.

1. If $\frac{4}{5}$ of a number is 16, what is $\frac{1}{5}$ of the number?   _____

What is the number?   _____

2. Our football team won $\frac{3}{4}$ of the games that it played.

It won 12 games. How many games did it play?   _____
(unit)

3. When a balloon had traveled 800 miles it had completed $\frac{2}{3}$ of its journey. What was the total length of its trip?   _____
(unit)

4. Neil's box of mixed fruit contains 15 oranges. These oranges are worth $\frac{3}{5}$ of the total number of pieces of fruit in the box. How many pieces of fruit does Neil have?   _____ pieces

5. Grandma baked cookies. Twenty cookies were oatmeal raisin. The oatmeal raisin cookies represent $\frac{5}{8}$ of all the cookies. How many cookies did Grandma bake?   _____ cookies

6. Tiana jogged $\frac{6}{8}$ of the way to school in 12 minutes. If she continues at the same speed, how long will her entire jog to school take?   _____ minutes

7. After 35 minutes, Hayden had completed $\frac{7}{10}$ of his math test. If he has a total of 55 minutes to complete the test, do you think he will finish on time?   _____

8. Ian bought a video game that was on sale for $45. He paid 75% of the original price. How much would the game have cost if it had not been on sale? $ _____

9. An ad for a computer printer stated that you could buy the printer for only $280, or 80% of the original price. What was the original price of the printer? $ _____

How much would you save? $ _____

Fraction Review

Write three equivalent fractions for each fraction.

1. $\frac{7}{8}$ _____

2. $\frac{3}{4}$ _____

3. $\frac{6}{12}$ _____

4. $\frac{2}{3}$ _____

Circle the fraction that is closer to $\frac{1}{2}$.

5. $\frac{3}{8}$ or $\frac{4}{5}$

6. $\frac{4}{7}$ or $\frac{5}{9}$

7. $\frac{7}{8}$ or $\frac{7}{9}$

8. $\frac{4}{10}$ or $\frac{7}{12}$

9. Explain how you found your answer for Problem 8.

_____

_____

_____

_____

_____

Solve. Write your answers in simplest form.

10. $\frac{3}{5} + \frac{9}{10} =$ _____

11. $\frac{2}{5} + \frac{1}{4} =$ _____

12. _____ $= \frac{5}{6} + \frac{3}{4}$

13. $\frac{7}{9} - \frac{1}{6} =$ _____

14. $8 - \frac{2}{3} =$ _____

15. $\frac{7}{8} - \frac{1}{6} =$ _____

16. $\frac{2}{3}$ of $\frac{1}{2}$ is _____.

17. $\frac{3}{4}$ of $\frac{2}{5}$ is _____.

18. $\frac{2}{7} * \frac{3}{4} =$ _____

19. $4 * \frac{5}{6} =$ _____

Name _____   Date _____   Time _____

Mixed Number Review

Fill in the missing numbers.

1. $3\frac{3}{8} = \frac{\square}{8}$ **2.** $6\frac{2}{3} = 5\frac{\square}{3}$

3. $4\frac{1}{4} = 3\frac{\square}{4}$ **4.** $\frac{\square}{5} = 3\frac{7}{5}$

Solve. Write your answers in simplest form.

5. $1\frac{3}{5} + 2\frac{1}{5} = $ _____   **6.** $3\frac{3}{8} - 1\frac{5}{8} = $ _____

7. $7\frac{4}{9} - 5\frac{8}{9} = $ _____   **8.** $3\frac{2}{7} + 1\frac{4}{5} = $ _____

9. $5\frac{2}{3} + 2\frac{3}{4} = $ _____   **10.** $4 - 1\frac{3}{4} = $ _____

11. $2\frac{2}{5} + 3\frac{3}{5} = $ _____   **12.** $4\frac{1}{4} + 5\frac{3}{4} = $ _____

13. $3 * 3\frac{3}{4} = $ _____   **14.** $4\frac{2}{3} * \frac{6}{7} = $ _____

15. _____ $= 2\frac{1}{2} * 1\frac{4}{5}$ **16.** $\frac{3}{10} * 8\frac{1}{3} = $ _____

Family Letter

Unit 9: Coordinates, Area, Volume, and Capacity

The beginning of this unit will provide your child with practice in naming and locating ordered number pairs on a coordinate grid. Whole numbers, fractions, and negative numbers will be used as coordinates. Your child will play the game *Hidden Treasure* (similar to the commercially available *Battleship*™), which provides additional practice with coordinates. You may wish to challenge your child to a round.

In previous grades, your child studied the perimeters (distances around) and the areas (amounts of surface) of geometric figures. *Fourth Grade Everyday Mathematics* developed and applied formulas for the areas of rectangles, parallelograms, and triangles. In this unit, your child will review these formulas and explore new area topics, including the rectangle method for finding areas of regular and irregular shapes.

Students will also examine how area, perimeter, and angle measurements are affected when a figure is changed by mathematical transformations. These transformations resemble changes and motions in the physical world. In some transformations, figures are enlarged in one or two dimensions; in other transformations, figures are translated (slid) or reflected (flipped over).

In the exploration "Earth's Water Surface," students review locating places on Earth with latitude and longitude. Then they use latitude and longitude in a sampling experiment that enables them to estimate, without measuring, the percent of Earth's surface that is covered by water. In a second exploration, "School's Land Area," students use actual measurements and scale drawings to estimate the land area covered by their school.

The unit concludes with a look at volume (the amount of space an object takes up) and capacity (the amount of material a container can hold). Students develop a formula for the volume of a prism (volume = area of the base * the height). They observe the metric equivalents 1 liter = 1,000 milliliters = 1,000 cubic centimeters, and they practice making conversions between U.S. customary measures (1 gallon = 4 quarts, and so on).

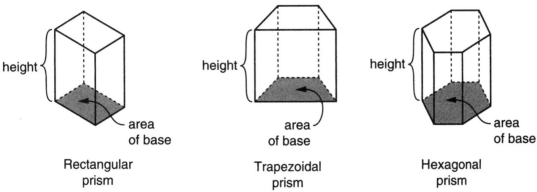

height {   area of base   Rectangular prism

height {   area of base   Trapezoidal prism

height {   area of base   Hexagonal prism

Please keep this Family Letter for reference as your child works through Unit 9.

Vocabulary

Important terms in Unit 9:

area The amount of surface inside a closed boundary. Area is measured in square units, such as square inches and square centimeters.

Two ways to model area

axis Either of the two number lines that intersect to form a coordinate grid.

capacity The amount a container can hold, usually in such units as *quart, gallon, cup,* and *liter.*

coordinate A number used to locate a point on a number line, or one of two numbers used to locate a point on a coordinate grid.

coordinate grid A device for locating points in a plane using ordered number pairs, or coordinates.

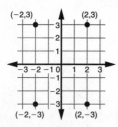

Coordinate grid

formula A general rule for finding the value of something. A formula is often written using letters, called *variables,* that stand for the quantities involved. For example, the formula for the area of a rectangle may be written as $A = l * w$, where A represents the area of the rectangle, l represents the length, and w represents the width.

height A measure of how tall something is. In geometry, height is the same thing as altitude.

latitude A measure, in degrees, of the distance of a place north or south of the Equator.

longitude A measure, in degrees, of how far east or west of the prime meridian a place is.

opposite of a number A number that is the same distance from zero on the number line as a given number, but on the opposite side of zero. For example, the opposite of +3 is −3 and the opposite of −5 is +5.

ordered number pair Two numbers that are used to locate a point on a *coordinate grid.* The first number gives the position along the horizontal axis; the second number gives the position along the vertical axis. Ordered number pairs are usually written in parentheses: (5,3).

perpendicular Meeting at right angles. Lines, rays, line segments, and planes that meet at right angles are perpendicular. The symbol ⊥ means "is perpendicular to."

rectangle method A method for finding area in which one or more rectangles are drawn around a figure or parts of a figure.

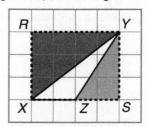
To find the area of triangle *XYZ,* subtract the areas of the two darkly shaded triangles from the area of rectangle *XRYS.*

transformation Something done to a geometric figure that produces a new figure. The most common transformations are translations (slides), reflections (flips), and rotations (turns).

variable A letter or symbol that represents a number. A variable can represent one specific number or it can stand for many different numbers.

volume The amount of space inside a 3-dimensional object. Volume is usually measured in cubic units, such as cubic centimeters, cubic inches, or cubic feet. Sometimes volume is measured in units of capacity, such as gallons or liters.

Use with Lesson 8.13.

Do-Anytime Activities

To work with your child on concepts taught in this unit, try these interesting and rewarding activities:

1 Find an atlas or map that uses letter-number pairs to locate places. (For example, an atlas might say that Chattanooga, Tennessee is located at D-9.) Use the letter-number pairs to locate places you have visited or would like to visit.

2 Estimate the area of a room in your home. Use a tape measure or ruler to measure the room's length and width, and multiply to find the area. Make a simple sketch of the room, including the length, the width, and the area. If you can, find the area of other rooms, or even of your entire home.

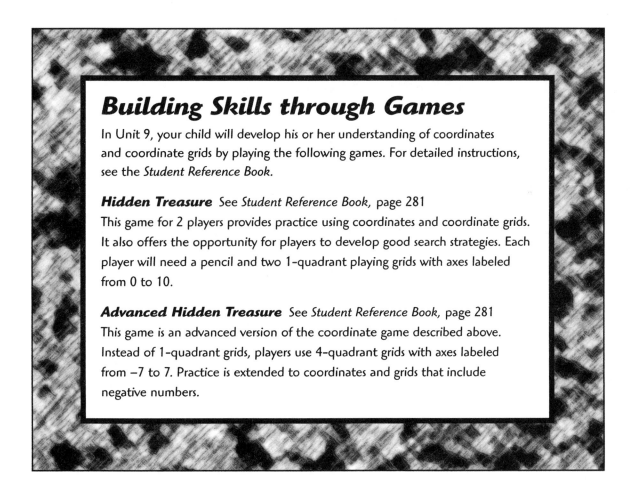

Building Skills through Games

In Unit 9, your child will develop his or her understanding of coordinates and coordinate grids by playing the following games. For detailed instructions, see the *Student Reference Book*.

Hidden Treasure See *Student Reference Book*, page 281
This game for 2 players provides practice using coordinates and coordinate grids. It also offers the opportunity for players to develop good search strategies. Each player will need a pencil and two 1-quadrant playing grids with axes labeled from 0 to 10.

Advanced Hidden Treasure See *Student Reference Book*, page 281
This game is an advanced version of the coordinate game described above. Instead of 1-quadrant grids, players use 4-quadrant grids with axes labeled from −7 to 7. Practice is extended to coordinates and grids that include negative numbers.

As You Help Your Child with Homework

As your child brings assignments home, you may want to go over the instructions together, clarifying them as necessary. The answers listed below will guide you through some of the Study Links in this unit.

Study Link 9.1

2. Rectangular prism

3. a. (11,7)

Study Link 9.3

2. The first number

3.

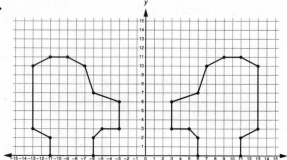

Study Link 9.4

1. $12\frac{1}{2}$ hr

2. 114 square feet

3. 80 yd^2 **4.** 33 ft^2

5.

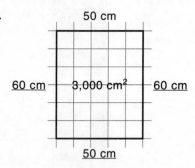

6.

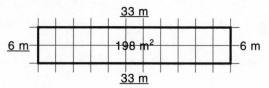

Study Link 9.5

1. 4 cm^2 **2.** 7.5 cm^2 **3.** 6 cm^2

4. 16 cm^2 **5.** 10 cm^2 **6.** 15 cm^2

Study Link 9.6

1. 4.5 cm^2; $\frac{1}{2} * 3 * 3 = 4.5$

2. 7.5 cm^2; $\frac{1}{2} * 5 * 3 = 7.5$

3. 3 cm^2; $\frac{1}{2} * 2 * 3 = 3$

4. 24 cm^2; $6 * 4 = 24$

5. 12 cm^2; $4 * 3 = 12$

6. 8 cm^2; $4 * 2 = 8$

Study Link 9.7

1. ft^2, yd^2 **2.** cm^2, in.^{2} **3.** cm^2

4. $A = \frac{1}{2} * b * h$; 130 ft^2 **5.** $A = b * h$; 16 cm^2

6. $A = \frac{1}{2} * b * h$; 77 yd^2 **7.** $A = b * h$; 76 m^2

Study Link 9.8

1. 15 cm^2; 15 cm^3; 45 cm^3 **2.** 8 cm^2; 8 cm^3; 16 cm^3

3. 9 cm^2; 9 cm^3; 27 cm^3 **4.** 14 cm^2; 14 cm^3; 56 cm^3

Study Link 9.9

1. 72 cm^3 **2.** 144 cm^3 **3.** 70 in.^{3}

4. 162 cm^3 **5.** 45 in.^{3} **6.** 140 m^3

Study Link 9.10

2. $A = \frac{1}{2} * 7 * 6$; 21 cm^2

3. $A = 8 * 6$; 48 in.^{2}

Reflections on a Grid

1. Plot the points listed below. Use a straightedge to connect the points in the same order that you plot them.

   (6,0); (6,2); (5,3); (3,3); (3,6); (6,7); (7,10); (9,11); (11,11); (13,10); (13,3); (11,2); (11,0)

2. Which number (the first number or the second number) in the pair do you need to change to the opposite in order to draw the reflection of this design on the other side of the *y*-axis?

   _____

3. Draw the reflection described above. Plot the points and connect them.

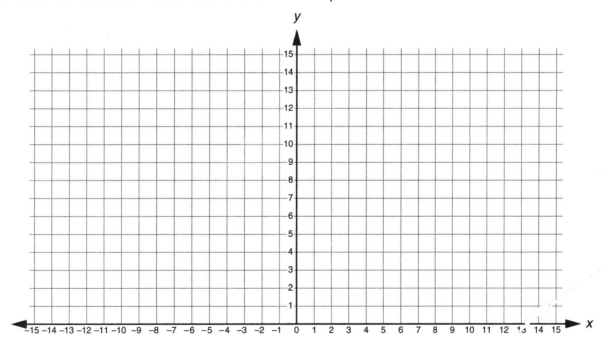

More Area Problems

1. Rashid can paint 2 square feet of fence in 10 minutes. How long
will it take him to paint a fence that is 6 feet high by 25 feet long?

_____

2. Regina wants to cover one wall of her room with wallpaper. The wall is
9 feet high and 15 feet wide. There is a doorway in the wall that is 3 feet
wide and 7 feet tall. How many square feet of wallpaper will she need to buy?

_____

Calculate the areas for the figures below.

3.

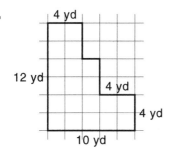

4 yd
12 yd
4 yd
4 yd
10 yd

4.

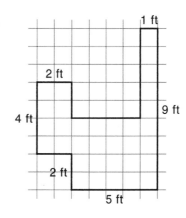

1 ft
2 ft
4 ft
9 ft
2 ft
5 ft

Area = _____ yd²

Area = _____ ft²

Fill in the missing lengths for the figures below.

5.

50 cm
3,000 cm²

6.

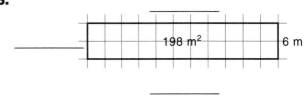

198 m²
6 m

7. On the back of this page, explain how you found the area for Problem 4.

Area Formulas

Area of a parallelogram: $A = b * h$

Area of a triangle: $A = \frac{1}{2} * b * h$

For each figure below, label the base and the height; find the area; and record the number model you used to find the area.

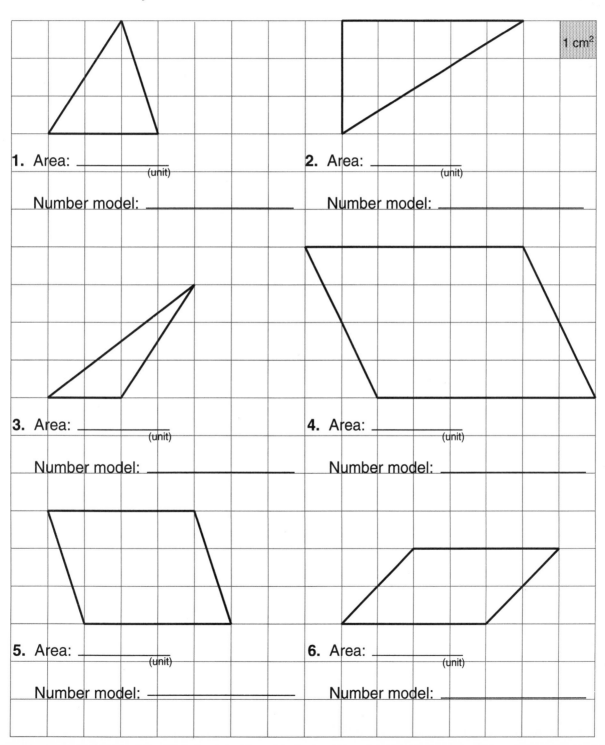

1 cm²

1. Area: _____
(unit)

Number model: _____

2. Area: _____
(unit)

Number model: _____

3. Area: _____
(unit)

Number model: _____

4. Area: _____
(unit)

Number model: _____

5. Area: _____
(unit)

Number model: _____

6. Area: _____
(unit)

Number model: _____

An Area Review

Circle the most appropriate unit or units to use for measuring the area of each object.

1. The area of a football field   cm²   ft²   yd²   in.²

2. The area of your hand   cm²   ft²   yd²   in.²

3. The area of a postage stamp   cm²   ft²   yd²   in.²

Find the area of the figures shown below.
Write the formula you used to find the area.

> Area of a triangle: $A = \frac{1}{2} * b * h$
>
> Area of a parallelogram: $A = b * h$

4.

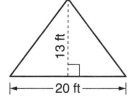

13 ft

20 ft

Formula: _____

Area: _____
(unit)

5.

8 cm

2 cm

Formula: _____

Area: _____
(unit)

6.

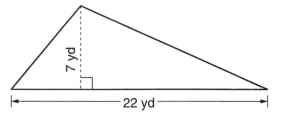

7 yd

22 yd

Formula: _____

Area: _____
(unit)

7.

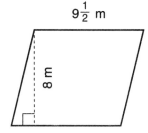

$9\frac{1}{2}$ m

8 m

Formula: _____

Area: _____
(unit)

Volumes of Prisms

The volume V of any prism can be found with the formula $V = B * h$, where B is the area of the base of the prism, and h is the height of the prism for that base.

1.

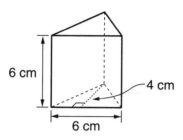

6 cm
4 cm
6 cm

Volume = _____ cm³

2.

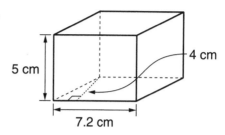

5 cm
4 cm
7.2 cm

Volume = _____ cm³

3.

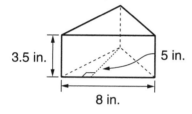

3.5 in.
5 in.
8 in.

Volume = _____ in.³

4.

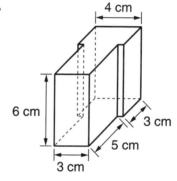

4 cm
6 cm
3 cm
5 cm
3 cm

Volume = _____ cm³

5.

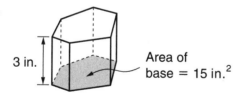

3 in.
Area of base = 15 in.²

Volume = _____ in.³

6.

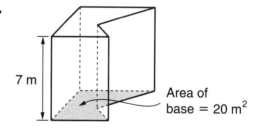

7 m
Area of base = 20 m²

Volume = _____ m³

Unit 9 Review

1. Plot 6 points on the grid below and connect them to form a hexagon.
List the coordinates of the points you plotted.

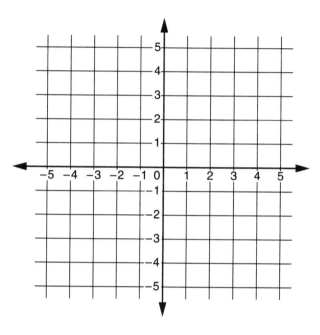

(_____ , _____)

(_____ , _____)

(_____ , _____)

(_____ , _____)

(_____ , _____)

(_____ , _____)

Find the area of the figures shown below.
Write the number model you used to
find the area.

Area of a rectangle: $A = b * h$

Area of a parallelogram: $A = b * h$

Area of a triangle: $A = \frac{1}{2} * b * h$

2.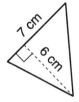

Number model: _____

Area: _____
            (unit)

3.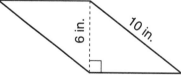

Perimeter = 36 in.

Number model: _____

Area: _____
            (unit)

4. On the back of this page, explain how you solved Problem 3.

Family Letter

Unit 10: Algebra Concepts and Skills

In this unit, your child will be introduced to solving simple equations with a pan balance, thus developing basic skills of algebra. For example, a problem might be to find how many marbles in the illustration below weigh as much as a cube. You can solve this problem by removing 3 marbles from the left pan and 3 marbles from the right pan. Then the pans will still balance. Therefore, you know that one cube weighs the same as 11 marbles.

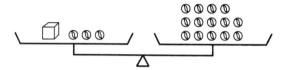

You can think of this pan-balance problem as a model for the equation $c + 3 = 14$, in which the value of c is 11.

A "What's My Rule?" table has been a routine since the early grades of *Everyday Mathematics*. In this unit, your child will follow rules to complete tables, such as the one below and will then graph the data. Your child will also determine rules from information provided in tables and graphs. Students will begin to express such rules using algebraic expressions containing variables.

Rule		in	out
out = in + 6		−1	5
		2	8
		5	
			12
		12	
			15

As the American Tour continues, your child will work with variables and formulas to predict eruption times of the famous geyser, Old Faithful, in Yellowstone National Park.

In previous grades, your child studied the perimeter (distance around) and the area (amount of surface) of geometric figures. In Unit 9, students developed and applied formulas for the area of rectangles, parallelograms, and triangles. In this unit, your child will explore and apply formulas for the circumference (distance around) and area of circles.

Please keep this Family Letter for reference as your child works through Unit 10.

Vocabulary

Important terms in Unit 10:

algebraic expression An expression that contains a variable. For example, if Maria is 2 inches taller than Joe, and if the variable *M* represents Maria's height, then the algebraic expression $M - 2$ represents Joe's height.

coordinate A number used to locate a point on a number line, or one of two numbers used to locate a point on a coordinate grid.

formula A general rule for finding the value of something. A formula is often written using letters, called *variables,* that stand for the quantities involved. For example, the formula for the area of a rectangle may be written as $A = l * w$, where *A* represents the area of the rectangle, *l* represents its length, and *w* represents its width.

line graph A graph in which data points are connected by line segments.

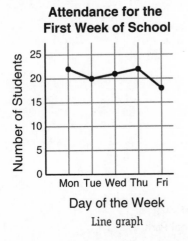

Attendance for the First Week of School

Line graph

ordered number pair Two numbers that are used to locate a point on a *coordinate grid.* The first number gives the position along the horizontal axis, and the second number gives the position along the vertical axis. The numbers in an ordered pair are called *coordinates.* Ordered pairs are usually written inside parentheses: (2,3).

Coordinate grid

pan balance A tool used to weigh objects or compare weights.

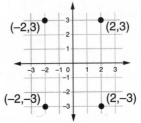

Pan balance

predict To tell what will happen ahead of time; to make an educated guess about what might happen.

rate A comparison by division of two quantities with unlike units. For example, a speed such as 55 miles per hour is a rate that compares distance with time.

variable A letter or other symbol that represents a number. A variable can represent one specific number or it can stand for many different numbers.

Do-Anytime Activities

To work with your child on concepts taught in this unit and in previous units, try these interesting and rewarding activities:

1 Have your child list different timed distances for a mile. For example, the fastest mile run by man and by a race car; your child's own fastest mile completed by running, biking, or walking; the fastest mile run for a handicapped athlete; the fastest mile completed by a swimmer, and so on.

2 Have your child keep a running tally of when the school bus arrives. Or have your child time himself or herself to see how long it takes to walk to school in the morning compared to walking home in the afternoon. After a week, have your child describe landmarks for their data, and interpret these landmarks.

Building Skills through Games

In this unit, your child will practice using algebraic expressions containing variables by playing the following game. For more detailed instructions, see the *Student Reference Book*.

First to 100 See *Student Reference Book*, page 273
This is a game for two to four players and requires 32 Problem Cards and a pair of six-sided dice. Players answer questions after substituting numbers for the variable on Problem Cards. The questions offer practice on a variety of mathematical topics.

As You Help Your Child with Homework

As your child brings assignments home, you may want to go over the instructions together, clarifying them as necessary. The answers listed below will guide you through some of the Study Links in this unit.

Study Link 10.1

1. 3   **2.** 3   **3.** 36   **4.** 4   **5.** 3

Study Link 10.2

1. 5, 10   **2.** 2, 2   **3.** 4, 6   **4.** true

5. true   **6.** false   **7.** false   **8.** 26

9. 2   **10.** 50   **11.** 0

Study Link 10.3

1.

in	out
−5	−11
8	2
10	4
2	−4
3	−3

2.

□	△
4	20
7	35
6	30
12	60
1.2, $\frac{6}{5}$, or $1\frac{1}{5}$	6
7.2, $\frac{36}{5}$, or $7\frac{1}{5}$	36

3.

in	out
−15	−7.5
37	44.5
−3.5	4
−20	−12.5

4.

□	△
3	21
2	$\frac{63}{2}$, 31.5, or $31\frac{1}{2}$
10	6.3, $\frac{63}{10}$, or $6\frac{3}{10}$
6	10.5
1	63

Study Link 10.4

1.

in (n)	out (15−n)
1	14
2	13
8	7
10	5
18	−3
15	0

3.

in (x)	out ((2 * x) + 3)
1	5
2	7
3	9
6	15
8	19
0	3

5. Rule: $(n * 2) − 1$; Multiply "in" by 2 and then subtract 1.

in	out
1	1
2	3
3	5
4	7
5	9
10	19

Study Link 10.5

1. 60°F   **2.** 72°F   **3. a.** 70°F   **b.** 67°F

4. Sample answer: Some types of crickets may chirp more slowly than others. The formulas predict higher temperatures for crickets that chirp at faster rates.

Study Link 10.6

°C	−20	−10	0	10	20	30
°F (formula)	−4	14	32	50	68	86
°F (rule of thumb)	−8	12	32	52	72	92

Study Link 10.7

Answers vary.

Study Link 10.8

1. a. 22.0   **b.** 40.2

2. a. 85   **b.** 85

3. a. 21

Study Link 10.9

1. circumference   **2.** area   **3.** area

4. circumference   **5.** 50 cm²

6. 6 in.   **7.** 5 m

8. Sample answer: The circumference is 31.4 meters, and this equals π * d, or about 3.14 * d. Since 3.14 * 10 = 31.4, the diameter is about 10 meters. The radius is half the diameter, or about 5 meters.

Use with Lesson 9.11.

Pan-Balance Problems

Solve these pan-balance problems. In each figure, the two pans are in perfect balance.

SRB
212 213

1. One triangle weighs

as much as _____ squares.

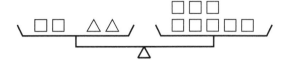

2. One cube weighs

as much as _____ marbles.

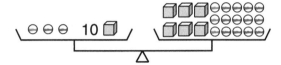

3. Two cantaloupes weigh

as much as _____ apples.

½ cantaloupe

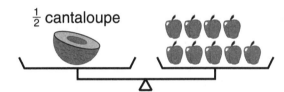

4. One *X* weighs

as much as _____ *Y*s.

| 4 *X*   15 *Y* | 6 *X*   7 *Y* |

5. One *B* weighs

as much as _____ *M*s.

| 3 *B*   3 *M* | 1 *B*   9 *M* |

More Pan-Balance Problems

In each figure below, the two pans are in perfect balance. Solve these
pan-balance problems.

1.

M weighs

as much as _____ marbles.

N weighs

as much as _____ marbles.

2.

   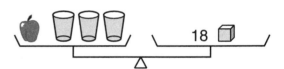

One △ weighs

as much as _____ □s.

One □ weighs

as much as _____ marbles.

3.

One cup of juice weighs

as much as _____ blocks.

One apple weighs

as much as _____ blocks.

True or false?

4. $(5 + 16) * 3 = 63$ _____

5. $30 = ((9 + 7) - 1) * 2$ _____

6. $38 = 2 + ((8 * 6) - 10)$ _____

7. $34 * (2 + 26) = 94$ _____

Fill in the missing numbers to make true sentences.

8. _____ $= (7 + 45) / 2$

9. $((28 / 7) + 12) / 8 =$ _____

10. $((14 * 3) + 14) - 6 =$ _____

11. _____ $= (3 - 3) * ((34 / 2) * 115)$

"What's My Rule?"

Complete each table according to the rule. Use a calculator if you wish.

1. Rule: Subtract 6 from the "in" number.

in	out
−5	−11
8	
10	
	−4
	−3

2. Rule: △ = 5 * □

□	△
4	
7	
6	
12	60
	6
	36

3. Rule: Add 7.5 to the "in" number.

in	out
−15	
37	
	4
−20	

4. Rule: △ = (9 * 7) / □

□	△
3	
2	
10	
	10.5
	63

"What's My Rule?"

Complete each table below according to the rule.

1. Rule: Subtract the "in" number from 15.

in (n)	out (15 − n)
1	
2	
8	
	5
18	
	0

2. Rule: Triple the "in" number.

in (d)	out (3 * d)
7	
12	
	24
0.3	
	1
$\frac{1}{2}$	

3. Rule: Double the "in" number and add 3.

in (x)	out ((2 * x) + 3)
1	
2	
3	
	15
8	
	3

Complete each table below. Write the rule in words or as a formula.

4. Rule: _____

_____

_____

in	out
6	3
9	$4\frac{1}{2}$
1	0.5
12	
	8
440	

5. Rule: _____

_____

_____

in	out
1	1
2	3
3	5
4	
5	
	19

6. Make up your own.

Rule: _____

_____

in	out

Cricket Formulas

In 1897, A. E. Dolbear, a physicist, published an article called "The Cricket as a Thermometer." In it he claimed that outside temperatures can be estimated by counting the number of chirps made by crickets and using the following formula:

Outside temperature (°F) = $\dfrac{\text{number of cricket chirps per minute} - 40}{4}$ + 50

1. According to this formula, what is the estimated outside temperature if you count 80 chirps in a minute? _____

Other cricket formulas exist. This one is supposed to work particularly well with field crickets:

Outside temperature (°F) = (number of chirps in 15 seconds) + 37

2. What outside temperature would be predicted if you counted 35 chirps in 15 seconds? _____

3. Compare the two formulas. If you counted 30 chirps in 15 seconds, what temperature would each formula predict?

a. First formula: _____

b. Second formula: _____

4. Why might the type of cricket you are listening to affect the accuracy of the prediction?

_____

_____

_____

_____

_____

Source: It's Raining Frogs and Fishes: Four Seasons of Natural Phenomena and Oddities of the Sky

Converting Celsius to Fahrenheit

In the U.S. customary system, temperature is measured in degrees Fahrenheit (°F). In the metric system, temperature is measured in degrees Celsius (°C). The temperature at which water freezes is 0°C, or 32°F.

You can use the following formula to convert temperatures measured in degrees Celsius to degrees Fahrenheit, where F stands for the number of degrees Fahrenheit and C for the number of degrees Celsius:

Formula: $F = (1.8 * C) + 32$

If you want to get a rough estimate of the temperature in degrees Fahrenheit, you can use the following rule of thumb:

Rule of thumb: Double the number of degrees Celsius and add the Fahrenheit freezing temperature.

$$F = (2 * C) + 32$$

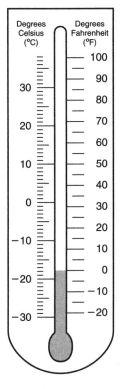

Convert the Celsius temperatures in the table to Fahrenheit temperatures, first using the formula and then the rule of thumb. Compare the results.

°C	−20	−10	0	10	20	30
°F (Use the formula.)						
°F (Use the rule of thumb.)						

Do you think that the results you get using the rule of thumb are close enough

in most situations? _____

Explain. _____

_____

If you were sick and you took your temperature with a Celsius thermometer, would you use the formula or the rule of thumb to convert your temperature

to degrees Fahrenheit? _____

Explain. _____

_____

Mystery Graphs

Create a mystery graph on the grid below. Be sure to label the horizontal and vertical axes. Describe the situation that goes with your graph on the lines provided.

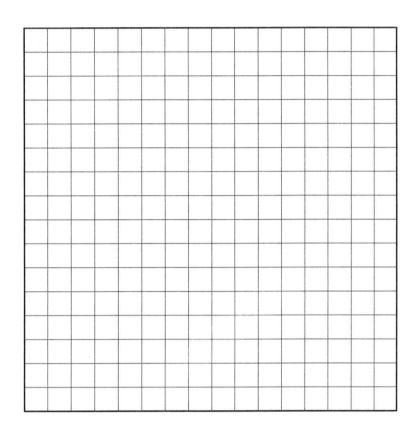

_____

_____

_____

_____

_____

_____

_____

_____

_____

Finding Circumferences

The formula for the circumference of a circle is:

> **Circumference = π * diameter** or just **C = π * d**

Use the π key on your calculator to solve these problems. If your calculator doesn't have a π key, enter 3.14 each time you need π.

1. Find the circumference of each circle below. Show answers to the nearest tenth.

a.

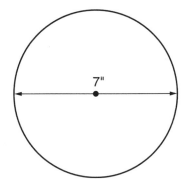

7"

b.

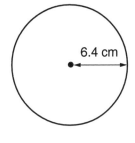

6.4 cm

Circumference ≈ _____ inches

Circumference ≈ _____ centimeters

2. The wheels on Will's bicycle have a diameter of about 27 inches, including the tire.

a. What is the circumference of the tire?

About _____ inches

b. About how far will Will's bicycle travel if the wheels go around exactly once?

About _____ inches

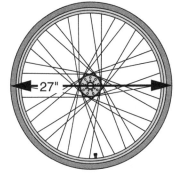

27"

3. Sofia measured the circumference of her bicycle tire. She found it was 66 inches. What is the diameter of the tire?

About _____ inches

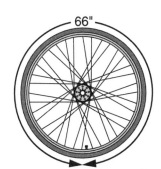

66"

Area and Circumference

Circle the best measurement for each situation described below.

1. What size hat to buy (*Hint:* The hat has to fit around the head.)

     area   circumference   perimeter

2. How much frosting covers the top of a round birthday cake

     area   circumference   perimeter

3. The amount of yard that will be covered by a circular inflatable swimming pool

     area   circumference   perimeter

4. The length of the top of a can label when you pull it off of the can

     area   circumference   perimeter

Fill in the oval next to the measurement that best completes each statement.

> Area of a circle: $A = \pi * r^2$
> Circumference of a circle: $C = \pi * d$

5. The radius of a circle is about 4 cm. The area of the circle is about

   O 12 cm^2 O 39 cm^2 O 50 cm^2 O 25 cm^2

6. The area of a circle is about 28 in.^{2}. The diameter of the circle is about

   O 3 in.   O 6 in.   O 9 in.   O 18 in.

7. The circumference of a circle is about 31.4 meters. The radius of the circle is about

   O 3 m   O 5 m   O 10 m   O 15 m

8. Explain how you found your answer for Problem 7.

_____

_____

_____

_____

_____

Unit 11: Volume

Unit 11 focuses on developing your child's ability to think spatially. Many times, students may feel that concepts of area and volume are of little use in their everyday lives compared with their computation skills. Encourage your child to become more aware of the importance and relevance of 2- and 3-dimensional shapes. Point out geometric solids (such as pyramids, cones, and cylinders) as well as 2-dimensional shapes (such as squares, circles, and triangles) in your surroundings.

Volume (or capacity) is the measure of the amount of space inside a 3-dimensional geometric figure. Your child will develop formulas to calculate the volume of rectangular and curved solids in cubic units. The class will also review units of capacity, such as cups, pints, quarts, and gallons. They will use units of capacity to estimate the volume of irregular objects by measuring the amount of water each object displaces when submerged. Your child will also explore the relationship between weight and volume by calculating the weight of rice an "average" Thai family of four consumes in one year and estimating how many cartons of a certain size would be needed to store a year's supply.

Area is defined as the number of units (usually squares) that can fit onto a bounded surface, without gaps or overlaps. Your child will review formulas for finding the area of rectangles, parallelograms, triangles, and circles and use these formulas in calculating the surface area of 3-dimensional shapes.

It is not the goal of this unit to have students memorize formulas, but rather to help them develop an appreciation for their use and application in various settings. By the end of this unit, your child will have had many experiences using 2- and 3-dimensional geometry.

Using a calibrated bottle, your child will
find the volume of an irregular object by
submerging it in water and measuring
the volume of water it displaces.

Please keep this Family Letter for reference as your child works through Unit 11.

Vocabulary

Important terms in Unit 11:

apex In a pyramid or cone, the vertex opposite the base.

base of a polygon A side on which a polygon "sits". The height of a polygon may depend on which side is called the base.

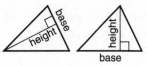

base of a prism or cylinder Either of the two parallel and congruent faces that define the shape of a prism or a cylinder.

base of a pyramid or cone The face of a pyramid or cone that is opposite its apex.

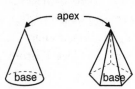

calibrate To divide or mark something, such as a thermometer, with gradations.

cone A 3-dimensional shape that has a circular *base*, a curved surface, and one vertex, which is called the *apex*.

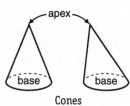

Cones

cube A polyhedron with 6 square faces. A cube has 8 vertices and 12 edges.

cylinder A 3-dimensional shape that has two circular or elliptical bases that are parallel and congruent and are connected by a curved surface. A can is shaped like a cylinder.

cylinder

edge A line segment where two faces of a polyhedron meet.

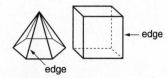

face A flat surface on a 3-dimensional shape.

geometric solid A 3-dimensional shape, such as a prism, pyramid, cylinder, cone, or sphere. Despite its name, a geometric solid is "hollow"; it does not contain the points in its interior.

polyhedron A closed 3-dimensional figure whose surfaces, or faces, are all formed by polygons and their interiors.

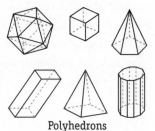

Polyhedrons

prism A solid with two parallel *faces*, called *bases*, that are congruent polygons; all of its other faces all parallelograms. Prisms get their names from the shapes of their bases.

 triangular prism   rectangular prism

pyramid A solid in which one face, the *base*, is any polygon and all the other faces are triangles that come together at a point called the *vertex* or *apex*. Pyramids get their names from the shapes of their bases.

 square pyramid

regular polyhedron A polyhedron whose faces are formed by a single kind of congruent regular polygon and in which every vertex looks exactly the same as every other vertex. There are five regular polyhedrons.

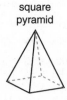 tetrahedron   cube   octahedron

  dodecahedron   icosahedron

sphere The set of all points in space that are a given distance from a given point. The given point is the center of the sphere and the given distance is the radius.

surface area A measure of the surface of a 3-dimensional figure.

vertex (vertices or vertexes) The point where the rays of an angle, the sides of a polygon, or the edges of a polyhedron meet.

 vertex
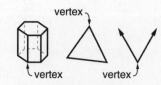 vertex   vertex

Use with Lesson 10.10.

Do-Anytime Activities

To work with your child on the concepts taught in this unit, try these interesting and rewarding activities:

1 Have your child compile a 2- and 3-dimensional shapes portfolio or create a collage of labeled shapes. Images can be taken from newspapers, magazines, photographs, and so on.

2 **Explore Kitchen Measures**
The most common use of measuring volume is cooking. Work with your child to make a favorite recipe. (Doubling the recipe can be good practice in computing with fractions.) Ask your child to use measuring spoons and cups to find the capacity of various containers. The data can be organized in a table:

Container	Capacity
Coffee mug	$1\frac{1}{4}$ cups
Egg cup	3 tablespoons

Building Skills through Games

In Unit 11, your child will practice operations with whole numbers and geometry skills by playing the following games. Detailed instructions for each game are in the *Student Reference Book.*

Name That Number See *Student Reference Book,* page 286
This is a game for two or three players using the Everything Math Deck or a complete deck of number cards. Playing *Name That Number* helps students review operations with whole numbers, including the order of operations.

Polygon Capture See *Student Reference Book,* page 289
This game uses 16 polygons and 16 Property Cards, and is played by partners or 2 teams each with 2 players. *Polygon Capture* gives students practice in identifying properties of polygons that involve sides and angles.

3-D Shape Sort See *Student Reference Book,* page 293
This game is similar to *Polygon Capture.* Partners or 2 teams each with 2 players need 16 Property Cards and 12 Shape Cards to play. *3-D Shape Sort* gives students practice in identifying properties of 3-dimensional shapes.

Use with Lesson 10.10.

As You Help Your Child with Homework

As your child brings assignments home, you may want to go over the instructions together, clarifying them as necessary. The answers listed below will guide you through some of this unit's Study Links.

Study Link 11.1

1. Answers vary.

2. D

Study Link 11.2

1. Rectangular prism: 6 faces; 8 vertices; 12 edges
   Tetrahedron: 4 faces; 4 vertices; 6 edges
   Triangular prism: 5 faces; 6 vertices; 9 edges
   Rectangular pyramid: 5 faces; 5 vertices; 8 edges
   Octahedron: 8 faces; 6 vertices; 12 edges

2. **a.** Sample answer: The sum of the numbers of faces and vertices is 2 more than the number of edges.

   b. $e = (f + v) - 2$

Study Link 11.3

Answers vary for Problems 1–4.

Study Link 11.4

1. <

2. <

3. >

4. Sample answer: Since both pyramids have the same height, compare the areas of the bases. The base of the square pyramid has an area of $5 * 5 = 25$ m^2. The base area of the triangular pyramid is $\frac{1}{2} * 5 * 5$, or $12\frac{1}{2}$ m^2.

5. **a.** Sample answer: Displacement means moving something out of its proper place.

   b. Sample answer: To calibrate is to divide or mark to show measurements, as on a thermometer.

Study Link 11.5

Sample answer: Cotton is not very dense, so it did not displace too much water.

Study Link 11.6

1. >   2. =   3. <

4. <   5. <   6. =

7. cubic inches

8. gallons

9. gallons

10. milliliters

11. cubic centimeters

12. capacity

13. volume

14. Sample answer: Capacity is a measure of how much of a pourable substance or liquid a container can hold. Volume is a measure of the amount of space occupied by a 3-dimensional shape.

Study Link 11.7

1. 88 in.^{2}; Sample answers: I found the area of each of the 6 sides and then the total. Or, I found the area of the top, front, and one side; I added these 3 areas and doubled the result.

2. Yes. A 4 in. $\times$ 4 in. $\times$ $3\frac{1}{2}$ in. box has a volume = 56 in.^{3} and surface area = 88 in.^{2}

3. Volume: 502.7 cm^3; Surface area: 351.9 cm^3

4. Volume: 216 in.^{3}; Surface area: 216 in.^{3}

Cube Patterns

There are four patterns below. Three of the patterns can be folded to form a cube.

1. Try to guess which one of the patterns below cannot be folded into a cube.

My guess: Pattern _____ (A, B, C, or D) cannot be folded into a cube.

2. Cut and fold the pattern to check your guess. Did you make the correct guess? If not, try other patterns until you find the one that does not form a cube.

My answer: Pattern _____ (A, B, C, or D)
cannot be folded into a cube.

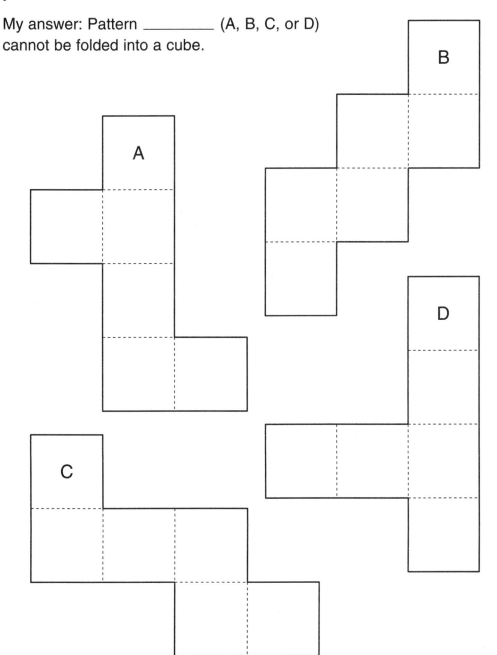

Faces, Vertices, and Edges

1. Refer to the pictures of polyhedrons on the next page to complete the following table:

SRB
137–138

Polyhedron	Number of Faces (*f*)	Number of Vertices (*v*)	Number of Edges (*e*)
Rectangular prism	6		
Tetrahedron		4	
Triangular prism			9
Rectangular pyramid			
Octahedron			

2. Look for a pattern in the results in your table.

   a. If you know the numbers of faces and vertices in a polyhedron, how can you calculate the number of edges, without counting them?

   _____

   _____

   _____

   b. Express your calculation as a formula. Let *f* represent the number of faces, let *v* represent the number of vertices, and let *e* represent the number of edges in the polyhedron.

   $e = $ _____

   c. Check that this formula is true for other polyhedrons.

   This formula is sometimes called Euler's Formula, named after the 18th-century Swiss mathematician and physicist, Leonhard Euler.

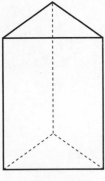

Triangular
Prism

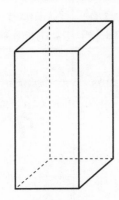

Rectangular
Prism

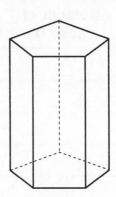

Pentagonal
Prism

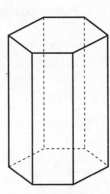

Hexagonal
Prism

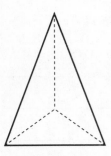

Triangular
Pyramid

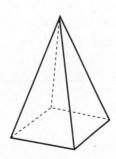

Rectangular (Square)
Pyramid

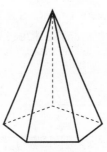

Pentagonal
Pyramid

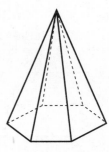

Hexagonal
Pyramid

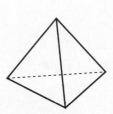

Tetrahedron

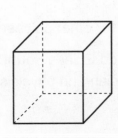

Cube

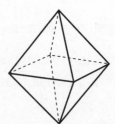

Octahedron

Volume of Cylinders

Use these two formulas to solve the problems below.

Formula for the Volume of a Cylinder	**Formula for the Area of a Circle**
$V = B * h$	$A = \pi * r^2$
where V is the volume of the cylinder, B is the area of the cylinder's base, and h is the height of the cylinder.	where A is the area of the circle and r is the length of the radius of the circle.

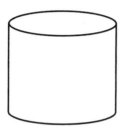
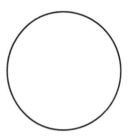

1. Find the smallest cylinder in your home. Record its dimensions and calculate its volume.

   radius = _____   height = _____

   Area of base = _____   Volume = _____

2. Find the largest cylinder in your home. Record its dimensions and calculate its volume.

   radius = _____   height = _____

   Area of base = _____   Volume = _____

3. Is the volume of the largest cylinder more or less than the volume of your toaster? _____

   About how much more or less? _____

4. Is the volume of the largest cylinder more or less than the volume of your television set? _____

   About how much more or less? _____

Comparing Volumes

Use >, <, or = to compare the volumes of the two figures in each problem below.

 SRB 180–183

1.

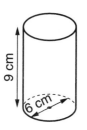

9 cm

6 cm

_____

9 cm

6 cm

6 cm

2.

24 ft

height of
base = 2 yd

3 yd

_____

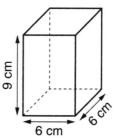

6 ft

8 yd

3.

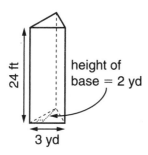

height = 6 m

base is
a square

5 m

5 m

_____

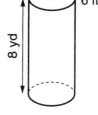

height = 6 m

height of
base = 5 m

5 m

4. Explain how you got your answer for Problem 3.

_____

_____

_____

_____

5. Use a dictionary to find the meaning(s) of each of the following words:

a. displacement: _____

_____

b. calibrate: _____

_____

A Displacement Experiment

Try this experiment at home.

Materials   ❑ drinking glass

❑ water

❑ 2 large handfuls of cotton (Be sure to use real cotton.
Synthetic materials will not work.)

Directions

• Fill the drinking glass almost to the top with water.

• Put the cotton bit by bit into the glass. Fluff it as you go.

If you are careful, you should be able to fit all of the cotton into the glass without spilling a drop of water.

Think about what you know about displacement and volume. Why do you think you were able to fit the cotton into the glass without the water overflowing?

_____

_____

_____

_____

_____

_____

_____

_____

_____

_____

_____

Units of Volume and Capacity

Write >, < , or = to compare the measurements below.

1. 5 cups _____ 1 quart   **2.** 30 mL _____ 30 cm³   **3.** 1 quart _____ 1 liter

4. 15 pints _____ 8 quarts   **5.** 100 cm³ _____ 1 gallon **6.** 10 cups _____ 5 pints

Circle the unit you would use to measure each of the following.

7. The volume of a square pyramid

gallons   cubic inches   ounces   meters

8. The amount of milk a fifth grader drinks in a week

gallons   milliliters   ounces   meters

9. The amount of water used to fill a swimming pool

gallons   milliliters   ounces   meters

10. The amount of penicillin given in a shot

gallons   milliliters   liters   meters

11. The volume of a rectangular prism

gallons   cubic centimeters   liters   meters

12. Would you find the **volume** or the **capacity** if
you wanted to know how much juice a jug holds? _____

13. Would you find the **volume** or the **capacity** if you wanted to
know how much closet space a stack of boxes would take up? _____

Challenge

14. Explain the difference between capacity and volume.

_____

_____

_____

_____

Volume and Surface Area

Area of rectangle:
  $A = l * w$

Volume of rectangular prism:
  $V = l * w * h$

Circumference of circle:
  $C = \pi * d$

Area of circle:
  $A = \pi * r^2$

Volume of cylinder:
  $V = \pi * r^2 * h$

SRB
181–182,
184–185

---

1. Marge wants to give her best friend a box of chocolates.
   Figure out the least number of square inches of wrapping
   paper Marge needs to wrap the box. (To simplify the
   problem, assume that she will cover the box completely,
   with no overlaps.)

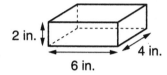

2 in.
6 in.
4 in.

   Amount of paper needed: _____

   Explain how you found the answer.

   _____

   _____

   _____

2. Could Marge use the same amount of wrapping paper to cover a box with a

   larger volume than the box pictured in Problem 1? _____ Explain.

   _____

   _____

Find the volume and the surface area of the two figures in Problems 3 and 4.

3. Volume:

   _____

   Surface area:

   _____

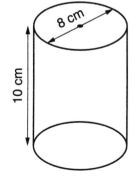

8 cm

10 cm

4. Volume:

   _____

   Surface area:

   _____

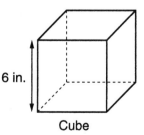

6 in.

Cube

Family Letter

Unit 12: Probability, Ratios, and Rates

A **ratio** is a comparison of two quantities with the same unit. For example, if one house has a floor area of 2,000 square feet, and a second house has a floor area of 3,000 square feet, the ratio of the areas is 2,000 to 3,000 or (simplified) 2 to 3.

To prepare students for working with ratios in algebra, the class will review the meanings and forms of ratios, and will solve number stories involving ratios of part of a set to the whole set. Your child will find, write, and solve many number models (equations) for ratio problems.

Your child will continue to use the American Tour as part of the discussion of ratios. We will also be doing projects based on information in the American Tour.

A **rate** is a comparison of two quantities with different units. For example, speed is expressed in miles per hour. In our study of rates, students will determine their own heart rates (heartbeats per minute). Then they will observe the effect of exercise on heart rate, and represent the class results graphically.

We will continue our study of probability by looking at situations in which a sequence of choices is made. For example, if a menu offers you 2 choices of appetizer, 4 choices of entrée, and 3 choices of dessert, and you choose one of each kind, there are $2 * 3 * 4$ or 24 different possible combinations for your meal. If all the choices were equally appealing (which is unlikely), and you chose at random, the probability of any one combination would be $\frac{1}{24}$.

Your child will play *Frac-Tac-Toe,* which was introduced in Unit 4, as well as a new game, *Spoon Scramble,* to practice operations and equivalencies with fractions, decimals, and percents.

You can help your child by asking questions about homework problems; by pointing out fractions, percents, and ratios that you encounter in everyday life; and by playing *Frac-Tac-Toe* or *Spoon Scramble* to sharpen skills.

Please keep this Family Letter for reference as your child works through Unit 12.

Vocabulary

Important terms in Unit 12:

common factor Any number that is a factor of two or more numbers. The common factors of 18 and 24 are 1, 2, 3, and 6.

equal chance or equally likely When each of the possible outcomes for some situation has the same chance of occurring, the outcomes are said to have an equal chance or to be equally likely. For example, in tossing a coin there is an equal chance of getting heads or tails. Heads and tails are equally likely outcomes.

factor tree A method used to obtain the prime factorization of a number. The original number is written as a product of factors. Then each of these factors is written as a product of factors, and so on, until the factors are all prime numbers. A factor tree looks like an upside down tree with the root (the original number) at the top, and the leaves (the factors) beneath it.

Factor tree for 30

greatest common factor The largest factor that two or more numbers have in common. For example, the common factors of 24 and 36 are 1, 2, 3, 4, 6, and 12. Thus, the greatest common factor of 24 and 36 is 12.

least common multiple The smallest number that is a multiple of two or more numbers. For example, while some common multiples of 6 and 8 are 24, 48, and 72, the least common multiple of 6 and 8 is 24.

multiplication counting principle A way of determining the total number of possible outcomes for two or more separate choices. Suppose, for example, you roll a die and then flip a coin. There are 6 choices for which face of the die shows and 2 choices for which side of the coin shows. Then there are 6 * 2, or 12 possible outcomes all together: (1,H), (1,T), (2,H), (2,T), (3,H), (3,T), (4,H), (4,T), (5,H), (5,T), (6,H), (6,T).

prime factorization A whole number expressed as a product of prime factors. For example, the prime factorization of 24 is 2 * 2 * 2 * 3.

probability A number from 0 to 1 that tells the chance that an event will happen. For example, the probability that a fair coin will show heads is $\frac{1}{2}$. The closer a probability is to 1, the more likely it is that the event will happen. The closer a probability is to 0, the less likely it is that the event will happen.

rate A comparison by division of two quantities with unlike units. For example, traveling 100 miles in 2 hours can be expressed as 100 mi/2 hr, or 50 miles per hour. In this case, the rate compares distance (miles) to time (hours).

ratio A comparison by division of two quantities with the same units. Ratios can be expressed as fractions, decimals, or percents, as well as in words. Ratios can also be written with a colon between the two numbers being compared. For example, if a team wins 3 out of 5 games played, the ratio of wins to total games can be written as $\frac{3}{5}$, 3/5, 0.6, 60%, 3 to 5, or 3:5 (read "three to five").

tree diagram A diagram such as a factor tree or a probability tree. A tree diagram is a network of points connected by line segments. One special point is the root of the tree and closed loops are not allowed. Tree diagrams can be used to factor numbers and to represent probability situations in which there is a series of events.

The first tree diagram below represents flipping one coin two times. The second tree diagram below shows the prime factorization of 30.

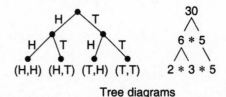

Tree diagrams

Use with Lesson 11.8.

Do-Anytime Activities

To work with your child on the concepts taught in this unit and in previous units, try these interesting and rewarding activities:

1 Identify different ratios and ask your child to write each ratio using words, a fraction, a decimal, a percent, and a colon. For example, the ratio of 1 adult for every 5 students could be written as 1 to 5, $\frac{1}{5}$, 0.2, 20%, or 1:5.

2 Play one of the games in this unit with your child: *Frac-Tac-Toe*, *Name That Number*, or *Spoon Scramble*.

3 Read the book *Jumanji* with your child and review the possible outcomes when rolling two dice. Ask your child to verify the probabilities of rolling certain number combinations by recording the outcomes for 100 rolls of a pair of dice.

4 Identify rate situations in everyday life and ask your child to solve problems involving rates. For example, find the number of miles your car travels for each gallon of gas, or find the number of calories that are burned each hour or minute for different types of sports activities.

Building Skills through Games

In Unit 12, your child will practice skills with probability, ratios, and rates by playing the following games. For detailed instructions, see the *Math Masters* and the *Student Reference Book*.

Frac-Tac-Toe See *Student Reference Book*, pp. 274–276
This is a game for two players. Game materials include 4 each of the number cards 0–10, pennies or counters of two colors, a calculator, and a gameboard. The gameboard is a 5-by-5 number grid that resembles a bingo card. Several versions of the gameboard are shown in the *Student Reference Book*. *Frac-Tac-Toe* provides students with practice in converting fractions to decimals and percents.

Name That Number See *Student Reference Book*, p. 286
This is a game for two or three players. Game materials include the Everything Math Deck or a complete deck of number cards. Playing *Name That Number* provides students with practice in working with operations and in using the order of operations.

Spoon Scramble See *Math Masters*, p. 174
This game provides students with practice identifying equivalent expressions for finding a fraction, decimal, or percent of a number. Four players use 3 spoons and a deck of 16 *Spoon Scramble* Cards to play this game.

As You Help Your Child with Homework

As your child brings assignments home, you may want to go over the instructions together, clarifying them as necessary. The answers listed below will guide you through this unit's Study Links.

Study Link 12.1   Sample answers:

1. a. 30
3 * 10
3 * 2 * 5

b. 45
5 * 9
5 * 3 * 3

2. a. $\frac{2}{3}$ **b.** $\frac{4}{9}$ **c.** $\frac{2}{3}$

3. 2 * 5 * 5 * 5

4. a. 32   **b.** 49   **5.** $\frac{2}{3}$

Study Link 12.2

1. 5 * 5 = 25

2.

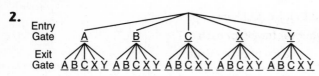

3. no; Sample answer: Some gates will probably be used more than other gates.

4. 20

5. a.

Question 1: R   W

Question 2: R   W   R   W

Question 3: R W R W R W R W

R = right answer   W = wrong answer

b. $\frac{1}{8}$

Study Link 12.3

1. Sixteen out of twenty-five

2. $\frac{16}{25}$ **3.** 64%   **4.** 16:25

5. 23:50; 0.46 of the cars were blue

6. $\frac{2}{3}$; 6:9; $66\frac{2}{3}$% of the people were swimmers

7. 7 out of 8; 35:40 of the caps sold were baseball caps

Study Link 12.4

1. a. 4   **b.** 16

2. 15

3. 16   **4.** 8   **5.** 32

Study Link 12.5

1. 8   **2.** 24   **3.** 45

4. 60   **5.** 20   **6.** 26

7. $\frac{2}{5} = \frac{\square}{115}$; 46 students

8. $\frac{3}{4} = \frac{\square}{156}$; 117 students

9. $\frac{1.50}{3} = \frac{\square}{90}$; $45

10. 210 tickets

Study Link 12.6

1. a.

Number of spiders	27,000	54,000	81,000	108,000	135,000
Pounds of spider web	1	2	3	4	5

b. 270,000

2. a.

Miles	13	26	39	52	65
Minutes	1	2	3	4	5

b. 780

3. 1,000   **4.** 930   **5.** $7\frac{1}{2}$, or 7.5

Study Link 12.8

3. 15 clarinetists

4. a. 12   **b.** 6   **c.** 4   **d.** 2

Use with Lesson 11.8.

Factor Trees

1. Make factor trees for the following numbers. An example has been done for you.

   20
   4 * 5
   2 * 2 * 5

   a.   30   **b.**   45

2. Write each fraction in simplest form. Use factor trees to help you.

   a. $\dfrac{20}{30} =$ _____   **b.** $\dfrac{20}{45} =$ _____   **c.** $\dfrac{30}{45} =$ _____

3. Find the prime factorization for 250. _____

4. **a.** Circle the number below that has the most prime factors. (You can use factor trees to help you.)

       63   32   49   100

   b. Which has the fewest prime factors? _____

Challenge

5. Simplify the fraction below. Use factor trees or some other method.

   $\dfrac{150}{225} =$ _____

Probability Investigations

Multiplication Counting Principle

SRB
124

Suppose you can make a first choice in *m* ways and a second choice in *n* ways. Then there are *m* * *n* ways to make the first choice followed by the second choice. Three or more choices can be counted in the same way, by multiplying.

1. A person can enter the stadium shown at the right through any gate, and can exit through any gate. In how many different ways can a person enter and exit the stadium?

A
B
C
X
Y

_____ * _____ = _____
(ways to enter)   (ways to exit)   (total ways to
                                      enter and exit)

2. Draw a **tree diagram** to show all possible ways to enter and exit the stadium.

Entry gate: ____   ____   ____   ____   ____

Exit gate: __ __ __ __ __   __ __ __ __ __   __ __ __ __ __   __ __ __ __ __   __ __ __ __ __

3. Do you think that all of the ways to enter and exit are equally likely? _____

   Explain your answer. _____

   _____

4. How many ways are there to enter and exit the same stadium if a person may not leave by the same gate through which he or she entered? _____

5. Sally takes a quiz with three true-false questions. She does not know the answer to any of the questions, so she guesses on all three.

   a. On the back of this page, draw a tree diagram to show Sally's possible results.

   b. What is the probability that she will get all three questions correct? _____

Ratios

Ratios can be stated or written in a variety of ways. Sometimes a ratio is easier to understand or will make more sense if it is rewritten in another form.

SRB 102

Example In a group of 25 students, 16 students walk to school and 9 take a bus. The ratio of students who take a bus, to all students in the group, can be expressed in the following ways:

- With words: Nine out of twenty-five students take a bus.

- With a fraction: $\frac{9}{25}$ of the students take a bus.

- With a percent: 36% of the students take a bus.

- With a colon between the two numbers being compared: The ratio of students who take a bus, to all students in the group, is 9:25 ("nine out of twenty-five").

Revise the above statements to express the ratio of students who walk to school, to all students.

1. With words: _____ students walk to school.

2. With a fraction: _____ of the students walk to school.

3. With a percent: _____ of the students walk to school.

4. With a colon: The ratio of students who walk to school to all students

is _____ .

In each problem, fill in the ovals next to all of the correct ratios.

5. Fifty cars drove past in 10 minutes. Twenty-three cars were blue.

　○ 23:50 of the cars were blue.　　○ 23% of the cars were blue.　　○ 0.46 of the cars were blue.

6. In a group of 9 people, 6 were swimmers.

　○ $\frac{2}{3}$ of the people were swimmers.　　○ 6:9 of the people were swimmers.　　○ $66\frac{2}{3}$% of the people were swimmers.

7. In a sports shop, 35 of the 40 caps sold the day before the World Series were baseball caps.

　○ 7 out of 8 caps sold were baseball caps.　　○ 35% of the caps sold were baseball caps.　　○ 35:40 of the caps sold were baseball caps.

Ratio Problems

1. Draw 20 tiles so that 2 out of 10 tiles are white and the rest are shaded.

   a. How many tiles are white? _____ tiles

   b. How many tiles are shaded? _____ tiles

2. Draw 9 shaded tiles.

   Add white tiles so that 2 out of 5 tiles are white.

   How many tiles are there in all? _____ tiles

3. Imagine 48 tiles. If 4 out of 12 tiles are white, how many tiles are white? _____ tiles

4. There are 24 players on the soccer team. Two out of every 3 players have not scored a goal yet this year.

   How many players have scored goals this year? _____ players

5. For every 8 spelling tests Justine took, she earned 3 perfect scores. If Justine earned

   12 perfect scores this year, how many spelling tests did she take? _____ tests

6. Make up and solve your own ratio number story. Be prepared to share it with the class.

   _____

   _____

   _____

   _____

   Answer: _____

Ratio Problems

Find the missing number.

1. $\dfrac{1}{5} = \dfrac{x}{40}$ $x =$ _____

2. $\dfrac{2}{3} = \dfrac{16}{y}$ $y =$ _____

3. $\dfrac{5}{6} = \dfrac{m}{54}$ $m =$ _____

4. $\dfrac{1}{4} = \dfrac{15}{n}$ $n =$ _____

5. $\dfrac{5}{8} = \dfrac{f}{32}$ $f =$ _____

6. $\dfrac{13}{50} = \dfrac{g}{100}$ $g =$ _____

Write a number model for each problem. Then solve the problem.

7. Of the 115 students in the sixth grade, 2 out of 5 belong to the Drama Club. How many students are members of the Drama Club?

Number model: _____   Answer: _____
                                                          (unit)

8. Three out of 4 students at Highland School ordered a hot lunch today. There are 156 students at the school. How many students ordered a hot lunch?

Number model: _____   Answer: _____
                                                          (unit)

9. Gina and the other members of her troop sell cookies for $3 a box. For each box they sell, the troop earns $1.50. One week, Gina's troop sold $90 worth of cookies. How much did the troop earn?

Number model: _____   Answer: $ _____

Challenge

10. 30% of the tickets sold by a movie theater for the Friday night show were children's tickets at $4 each. The rest of the tickets were sold at the full price of $8.50. The movie theater collected $252 for the children's tickets.

How many tickets did they sell in all?   Answer: _____
                                                                                          (unit)

On the back of this page, explain or show how you got your answer.

Rates

Complete each table using the given information. Then answer the question below each table.

1. a. It would take 27,000 spiders, each spinning a single web, to produce a pound of spider web.

Number of Spiders	27,000	54,000			
Pounds of Spider Web	1	2	3	4	5

b. At this rate, how many spiders, each spinning a single web,

would be needed to produce 10 pounds of spider web? _____ spiders

2. a. The deer botfly flies so fast that it is almost invisible to the human eye. In 1 minute it can travel 13 miles.

Miles	13				
Minutes	1	2	3	4	5

b. At this rate, how far could a deer botfly travel in 1 hour? _____ miles

Solve the following rate problems. Make a table if it will help you.

3. About 50 gallons of maple sap are needed to make 1 gallon of maple syrup. How many gallons of maple sap are needed to make 20 gallons of maple syrup?

About _____ gallons

4. For 186 days a year, the sun is not visible at the North Pole. During a 5-year period, for about how many days is the sun not visible?

About _____ days

5. In a beehive, about $1\frac{1}{2}$ ounces of beeswax are used to build a honeycomb that holds 4 pounds of honey. How much beeswax is needed to build a honeycomb that could hold 20 pounds of honey?

About _____ ounces

Source: 2201 Fascinating Facts

Rate and Pan-Balance Problems

1. The average American eats about 250 eggs per year. At this rate, about how many eggs will the average American eat in

   a. five years? _____

   (unit)

   b. $\frac{1}{12}$ of a year? _____

   (unit)

2. The average fifth grader can eat $\frac{3}{8}$ of a pizza for lunch. At this rate, how many lunches will it take for an average fifth grader to eat the equivalent of

   3 whole pizzas? _____

   (unit)

3. In 1975, a man in Washington state ate 424 clams in 8 minutes. At this rate, how many would he eat

   a. in $\frac{1}{4}$ of this time? _____

   (unit)

   b. in $2\frac{1}{2}$ times as much time? _____

   (unit)

Solve the following pan-balance problems.

4.

One circle weighs

as much as _____ triangles.

One square weighs

as much as _____ triangles.

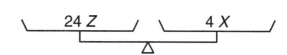

5.

One X weighs

as much as _____ Ys.

One Y weighs

as much as _____ Zs.

Musical Ratios

Piano/Keyboard	21 million
Guitar	19 million
Organ	6 million
Flute	4 million
Clarinet	4 million
Drums	3 million
Trumpet	3 million
Violin	2 million
Harmonica	1.7 million
Saxophone	1 million

At the left is a list of musical instruments played by people living in the United States and the approximate number of these people who play each instrument.

Source: America by the Numbers

1. a. What is the ratio of flute players to harmonica players? _____

    b. What is the ratio of drum players to piano players? _____

    c. Record the ratio of violin and saxophone players to trumpet players. _____

2. Which two pairs of instrument players have a 1-to-1 ratio? _____

_____

3. In a fifth-grade band, the ratio of saxophonists to clarinetists is 2:3. If there are 10 saxophonists, how many clarinetists are there? _____

Challenge

4. The school orchestra is performing tonight. There are 24 orchestra members. There are 6 violas. The ratio of violins to violas is 2:1. The ratio of cellos to basses is 2:1. There are no other instruments. How many chairs are needed in each section?

    a. Violins _____   **b.** Violas _____

    c. Cellos _____   **d.** Basses _____

Operations with Fractions

1. In the Malagasay Indian tribes, it is against the law for a son to be taller than his father. If a son is taller, he must give his father money or an ox. Suppose a father is 5 feet $10\frac{1}{2}$ inches tall and his son is 5 feet $6\frac{3}{4}$ inches tall. How many more inches can the son grow before he is as tall as his father?

_____
(unit)

2. In the state of Indiana, it is illegal to travel on a bus within 4 hours of eating garlic. If you lived in Indiana and had eaten a bowl of pasta with garlic bread $2\frac{1}{3}$ hours ago, how many more hours would you need to wait before you could legally travel on a bus?

_____
(unit)

3. In Idaho, it is against the law to give a person a box of candy that weighs more than 50 pounds. It is Valentine's Day, and you give your mother a box of candy that weighs $48\frac{1}{4}$ pounds. How much more could the box weigh without breaking the law?

_____
(unit)

4. The body of an average jellyfish is about $\frac{9}{10}$ water. What fraction of the jellyfish is not water?

_____

5. The world record for a jump by a frog is 19 feet $3\frac{1}{8}$ inches. How much farther would a frog need to jump to set a new world record of 7 yards?

_____
(unit)

6. The maximum length for a typical king cobra is about $5\frac{4}{5}$ meters. If 6 of these snakes were lined up end to end, how far would they stretch?

_____
(unit)

7. An average trumpeter swan weighs about $16\frac{4}{5}$ kilograms. What is the approximate weight of 3 average trumpeter swans?

_____
(unit)

Sources: The Top 10 of Everything; Beyond Belief!

End-of-Year Family Letter

Congratulations!

By completing *Fifth Grade Everyday Mathematics*, your child has accomplished a great deal. Thank you for all of your support!

This Family Letter is here for you to use as a resource throughout your child's vacation. It includes an extended list of Do-Anytime Activities, directions for games that can be played at home, a list of mathematics-related books to check out over vacation, and a sneak preview of what your child will be learning in *Sixth Grade Everyday Mathematics*. Enjoy your vacation!

Do-Anytime Activities

Mathematics means more when it is rooted in real-life situations. To help your child review many of the concepts he or she has learned in fifth grade, we suggest the following activities for you and your child to do together over vacation. These activities will help your child build on the skills he or she has learned this year and help prepare him or her for *Sixth Grade Everyday Mathematics*.

1 Review multiplication facts. Include the basic facts such as $7 * 8 = 56$, and "extended facts," such as $70 * 8 = 560$ and $70 * 80 = 5,600$.

2 Create opportunities to work with rulers, yardsticks, metersticks, tape measures, and scales. Have your child measure using both metric and U.S. customary units.

3 Ask your child to solve multiplication and division problems that are based on real-life situations. Vary the problems so that some are suitable for mental computation, some require paper-and-pencil calculation, and others require the use of a calculator.

4 Practice using percents by asking your child to calculate sales tax, percent discounts, sports statistics, and so on.

5 Continue the American Tour by reading about important people, events, inventions, explorations, and other topics in American history. Focus on data displays such as bar, line, and circle graphs; and on color-coded maps.

1	2	2	2	2	2
2	3	3	3	3	3
3	4	4	4	4	5
5	5	5	6	6	7
7	8	8	9	9	10
10	11	12	13	14	15
16	18	20	21	22	24
25	26	27	28	30	32

Factor Captor
number grid

Building Skills through Games

The following section lists rules for games that can be played at home. The number
cards used in some games can be made from 3" by 5" index cards.

Factor Captor

1. To start the first round, Player 1 (James) chooses a 2-digit number on the number
   grid. James covers it with a counter, and records the number on scratch paper.
   This is James's score for the round.

2. Player 2 (Emma) covers all of the factors of James's number. Emma finds the sum
   of the factors, and records it on scratch paper. This is Emma's score for the round.

   A factor may only be covered once during a round.

3. If Emma missed any factors, James can cover them with counters and add them to
   his score.

4. In the next round, players switch roles. Player 2 (Emma) chooses a number that is
   not covered by a counter. Player 1 (James) covers all factors of that number.

5. Any number that is covered by a counter is no longer available and may not be
   used again.

6. The first player in a round may not cover a number less than 10, unless no other
   numbers are available.

7. Play continues with players trading roles in each round, until all numbers on the
   grid have been covered. Players then use their calculators to find their total
   scores. The player with the higher total score wins the game.

EXAMPLE

Round 1: James covers 27 and scores 27 points. Emma covers 1, 3, and 9, and
scores 1 + 3 + 9 = 13 points.

Round 2: Emma covers 18 and scores 18 points. James covers 2, 3, and 6, and
scores 2 + 3 + 6 =11 points. Emma covers 9 with a counter, because 9 is also
a factor of 18. Emma adds 9 points to her score.

Frac-Tac-Toe (2-4-5-10 version)

Advance Preparation: Separate the cards into two piles—a numerator pile and a
denominator pile. For a 2-4-5-10 game, place two each of the 2, 4, 5, and
10 cards in the denominator pile. All other cards are placed on the numerator pile.

Shuffle the cards in each pile. Place the piles facedown. When the numerator pile is
completely used, reshuffle that pile, and place it facedown. When the denominator
pile is completely used, turn it over and place it facedown without reshuffling it.

1. Players take turns. When it is your turn:

   ▷ Turn over the top card from each pile to form a fraction
     (numerator card over denominator card).

   ▷ Try to match the fraction shown with one of the grid squares on
     the Game Board. (Use either of the gameboards shown) If a match
     is found, cover that grid square with your counter and your turn
     is over. If no match is found, your turn is over.

Game Boards for the 2-4-5-10
versions of *Frac-Tac-Toe*

>1.0	0 or 1	>2.0	0 or 1	>1.0
0.1	0.2	0.25	0.3	0.4
>1.5	0.5	>1.5	0.5	>1.5
0.6	0.7	0.75	0.8	0.9
>1.0	0 or 1	>2.0	0 or 1	>1.0

>100%	0% or 100%	>200%	0% or 100%	>100%
10%	20%	25%	30%	40%
>100%	50%	>200%	50%	>100%
60%	70%	75%	80%	90%
>100%	0% or 100%	>200%	0% or 100%	>100%

Use with Lesson 12.10.

2. To change the fraction shown by the cards to a decimal or percent, players *may* use a calculator.

3. Scoring The first player covering three squares in a row in any direction (horizontal, vertical, diagonal) is the winner.

Variations:

▷ For a 2-4-8 game, place two each of the 2, 4, and 8 cards in the denominator pile. Use the game boards shown in the margin.

▷ For a 3-6-9 game, place two each of the 3, 6, and 9 cards in the denominator pile. Use the game boards shown in the margin.

Multiplication Bull's-eye

1. Shuffle a deck of number cards (4 each of the numbers 0–9) and place them facedown on the playing surface.

2. Players take turns. When it is your turn:

▷ Roll a six-sided die. Look up the target range of the product in the table.

▷ Take four cards from the top of the deck.

▷ Use the cards to try to form two numbers whose product falls within the target range. **Do not use a calculator.**

▷ Multiply the two numbers on your calculator to determine whether the product falls within the target range. If it does, you have hit the bull's-eye and score 1 point. If it doesn't, you score 0 points.

▷ Sometimes it is impossible to form two numbers whose product falls within the target range. If this happens, you score 0 points for that turn.

3. The game ends when each player has had five turns.

4. The player scoring more points wins the game.

EXAMPLE

Tom rolls a 3, so the target range of the product is from 1,001 to 3,000.

He turns over a 5, a 7, a 2, and a 9.

Tom uses estimation to try to form two numbers whose product falls within the target range— for example, 97 and 25.

He finds the product on the calculator: $97 * 25 = 2,425$.

Since the product is between 1,001 and 3,000, Tom has hit the bull's-eye and scores 1 point.

Some other possible winning products from the 5, 7, 2, and 9 cards are: $25 * 79$, $27 * 59$, $9 * 257$, and $2 * 579$.

Number on Die	Target Range of Product
1	500 or less
2	501–1,000
3	1,001–3,000
4	3,001–5,000
5	5,001–7,000
6	more than 7,000

2-4-8 Frac-Tac-Toe Game Boards

>2.0	0 or 1	>1.5	0 or 1	>2.0
1.5	0.125	0.25	0.375	1.5
>1.0	0.5	0.25 or 0.75	0.5	>1.0
2.0	0.625	0.75	0.875	2.0
>2.0	0 or 1	1.125	0 or 1	>2.0

>200%	0% or 100%	>150%	0% or 100%	>200%
150%	$12\frac{1}{2}\%$	25%	$37\frac{1}{2}\%$	150%
>100%	50%	25% or 75%	50%	>100%
200%	$62\frac{1}{2}\%$	75%	$87\frac{1}{2}\%$	200%
>200%	0% or 100%	$112\frac{1}{2}\%$	0% or 100%	>200%

3-6-9 Frac-Tac-Toe Game Boards

>1.0	0 or 1	$0.\overline{1}$	0 or 1	>1.0
$0.1\overline{6}$	$0.\overline{2}$	$0.\overline{3}$	$0.\overline{3}$	$0.\overline{4}$
>2.0	$0.\overline{5}$	>1.0	$0.\overline{6}$	>2.0
$0.\overline{6}$	$0.\overline{7}$	$0.8\overline{3}$	$0.\overline{8}$	$1.\overline{3}$
>1.0	0 or 1	$1.\overline{6}$	0 or 1	>1.0

>100%	0% or 100%	11.1%	0% or 100%	>100%
$16\frac{2}{3}\%$	22.2%	$33\frac{1}{3}\%$	33.3%	44.4%
>200%	55.5%	>100%	66.6%	>200%
$66\frac{2}{3}\%$	77.7%	$83\frac{1}{3}\%$	88.8%	$133\frac{1}{3}\%$
>100%	0% or 100%	$166\frac{2}{3}\%$	0% or 100%	>100%

Vacation Reading with a Mathematical Twist

Books can contribute to children's learning by presenting mathematics in a combination of real-world and imaginary contexts. The titles listed below were recommended by teachers who use *Everyday Mathematics* in their classrooms. They are organized by mathematical topic. Visit your local library and check out these mathematics-related books with your child.

Numeration

The Rajah's Rice: A Mathematical Folktale from India by David Barry

Operations and Computation

Counting on Frank by Rod Clement

Data and Chance

Jumanji by Chris Van Allsburg

Geometry

A Cloak for the Dreamer by Aileen Friedman; *Flatland* by Edwin Abbott; *The Boy Who Reversed Himself* by William Sleator

Measurement and Reference Frames

Spaghetti and Meatballs for All!: A Mathematical Story by Marilyn Burns; *Mr. Archimedes' Bath* by Pamela Allen

Looking Ahead: Sixth Grade Everyday Mathematics

Next year your child will ...

▷ continue to collect, display, describe, and interpret data

▷ maintain and extend skills for comparing, adding, subtracting, multiplying, and dividing fractions and mixed numbers

▷ use scientific notation to write large and small numbers; explore scientific notation on a calculator

▷ continue the study of variables, expressions, equations, and other topics in algebra; use variables in spreadsheets; and solve equations and inequalities

▷ extend skills in geometry, including constructions, transformations of figures, and volumes of 3-dimensional figures

▷ maintain and apply skills for adding, subtracting, multiplying, and dividing whole numbers, decimals, and positive and negative numbers

Use with Lesson 12.10.